Putting **Essential Understanding** of

Geometry and Measurement

into **Practice**

in Grades
3–5

Kathryn Chval
University of Missouri
Columbia, Missouri

John Lannin
University of Missouri
Columbia, Missouri

Dusty Jones
Sam Houston State University
Huntsville, Texas

Kathryn Chval
Volume Editor
University of Missouri
Columbia, Missouri

Barbara J. Dougherty
Series Editor
University of Missouri
Columbia, Missouri

NATIONAL COUNCIL OF
TEACHERS OF MATHEMATICS

more**4u**
www.nctm.org/more4u
Access code: GAM14543

Copyright © 2016 by
The National Council of Teachers of Mathematics, Inc.
1906 Association Drive, Reston, VA 20191-1502
(703) 620-9840; (800) 235-7566; www.nctm.org
All rights reserved

Library of Congress Cataloging-in-Publication Data

Chval, Kathryn B. (Kathryn Bouchard)
  Putting essential understanding of geometry and measurement into practice in grades
3–5 / by Kathryn Chval, University of Missouri, Columbia, Missouri, John Lannin,
University of Missouri, Columbia, Missouri, and Dusty Jones, Sam Houston State
University, Huntsville, Texas.
        pages   cm. – (Putting essential understanding into practice series)
  Includes bibliographical references.
  ISBN 978-0-87353-733-9
  1. Geometry–Study and teaching (Primary) 2. Geometry–Study and teaching (Elementary)
3. Mathematics–Study and teaching (Primary) 4. Mathematics–Study and teaching
(Elementary) I. Lannin, John K. II. Jones, Dusty. III. Title.
  QA462.C48 2015
  372.7'6049--dc23
                                    2015027798

The National Council of Teachers of Mathematics is the public voice of mathematics education, providing vision, leadership, and professional development to support teachers in ensuring equitable mathematics learning of the highest quality for all students.

Printed in the United States of America

Contents

Accompanying Materials at More4U

Foreword

Teaching mathematics in prekindergarten–grade 12 requires knowledge of mathematical content and developmentally appropriate pedagogical knowledge to provide students with experiences that help them learn mathematics with understanding, while they reason about and make sense of the ideas that they encounter.

In 2010 the National Council of Teachers of Mathematics (NCTM) published the first book in the Essential Understanding Series, focusing on topics that are critical to the mathematical development of students but often difficult to teach. Written to deepen teachers' understanding of key mathematical ideas and to examine those ideas in multiple ways, the Essential Understanding Series was designed to fill in gaps and extend teachers' understanding by providing a detailed survey of the big ideas and the essential understandings related to particular topics in mathematics.

The Putting Essential Understanding into Practice Series builds on the Essential Understanding Series by extending the focus to classroom practice. These books center on the pedagogical knowledge that teachers must have to help students master the big ideas and essential understandings at developmentally appropriate levels.

To help students develop deeper understanding, teachers must have skills that go beyond knowledge of content. The authors demonstrate that for teachers—

- understanding student misconceptions is critical and helps in planning instruction;

- knowing the mathematical content is not enough—understanding student learning and knowing different ways of teaching a topic are indispensable;

- constructing a task is important because the way in which a task is constructed can aid in mediating or negotiating student misconceptions by providing opportunities to identify those misconceptions and determine how to address them.

Through detailed analysis of samples of student work, emphasis on the need to understand student thinking, suggestions for follow-up tasks with the potential to move students forward, and ideas for assessment, the Putting Essential Understanding into Practice Series demonstrates best practice for developing students' understanding of mathematics.

The ideas and understandings that the Putting Essential Understanding into Practice Series highlight for student mastery are also embodied in the Common Core State

Standards for Mathematics, and connections with these new standards are noted throughout each book.

On behalf of the Board of Directors of NCTM, I offer sincere thanks to everyone who has helped to make this new series possible. Special thanks go to Barbara J. Dougherty for her leadership as series editor and to all the authors for their work on the Putting Essential Understanding into Practice Series. I join the project team in welcoming you to this special series and extending best wishes for your ongoing enjoyment—and for the continuing benefits for you and your students—as you explore Putting Essential Understanding into Practice!

Linda M. Gojak
President, 2012–2014
National Council of Teachers of Mathematics

Preface

The Putting Essential Understanding into Practice Series explores the teaching of mathematics topics in grades K–12 that are difficult to learn and to teach. Each volume in this series focuses on specific content from one volume in NCTM's Essential Understanding Series and links it to ways in which those ideas can be taught successfully in the classroom.

Thus, this series builds on the earlier series, which aimed to present the mathematics that teachers need to know and understand well to teach challenging topics successfully to their students. Each of the earlier books identified and examined the big ideas related to the topic, as well as the "essential understandings"–the associated smaller, and often more concrete, concepts that compose each big idea.

Taking the next step, the Putting Essential Understanding into Practice Series shifts the focus to the specialized pedagogical knowledge that teachers need to teach those big ideas and essential understandings effectively in their classrooms. The Introduction to each volume details the nature of the complex, substantive knowledge that is the focus of these books–*pedagogical content knowledge*. For the topics explored in these books, this knowledge is both student centered and focused on teaching mathematics through problem solving.

Each book then puts big ideas and essential understandings related to the topic under a high-powered teaching lens, showing in fine detail how they might be presented, developed, and assessed in the classroom. Specific tasks, classroom vignettes, and samples of student work serve to illustrate possible ways of introducing students to the ideas in ways that will enable students not only to make sense of them now but also to build on them in the future. Items for readers' reflection appear throughout and offer teachers additional opportunities for professional development.

The final chapter of each book looks at earlier and later instruction on the topic. A look back highlights effective teaching that lays the earlier foundations that students are expected to bring to the current grades, where they solidify and build on previous learning. A look ahead reveals how high-quality teaching can expand students' understanding when they move to more advanced levels.

Each volume in the Putting Essential Understanding into Practice Series also includes three appendixes to extend and enrich readers' experiences and possibilities for using the book. The appendixes list the big ideas and essential understandings related to the topic, detail resources for teachers, and present tasks discussed in the book. These materials are also available to readers online at the More4U website, where Appendix 3 includes materials and templates to facilitate hands-on work with students. Readers can gain online access to each book's More4U materials by going to www.nctm.org/more4u and entering the code that appears on the title page. They can then print out these materials for personal or classroom use.

Because the topics chosen for both the earlier Essential Understanding Series and this successor series represent areas of mathematics that are widely regarded as challenging to teach and to learn, we believe that these books fill a tangible need for teachers. We hope that as you move through the tasks and consider the associated classroom implementations, you will find a variety of ideas to support your teaching and your students' learning.

Acknowledgments

We would like to thank the administrators and teachers at Paxton-Keeley Elementary School and Littlewood Elementary School for collaborating with us on the material for this volume. We would also like to thank their third-, fourth-, and fifth-grade students who shared their mathematical thinking with us. In addition, we extend thanks to Chris Bowling for his assistance in creating figures and scanning students' work and Lina Trigos-Carrillo for her assistance with compiling references.

Introduction

Shulman (1986, 1987) identified seven knowledge bases that influence teaching:

1. Content knowledge

2. General pedagogical knowledge

3. Curriculum knowledge

4. Knowledge of learners and their characteristics

5. Knowledge of educational contexts

6. Knowledge of educational ends, purposes, and values

7. Pedagogical content knowledge

The specialized content knowledge that you use to transform your understanding of mathematics content into ways of teaching is what Shulman identified as item 7 on this list—*pedagogical content knowledge* (Shulman 1986). This is the knowledge that is the focus of this book—and all the volumes in the Putting Essential Understanding into Practice Series.

Pedagogical Content Knowledge

In mathematics teaching, pedagogical content knowledge includes at least four indispensable components:

1. Knowledge of curriculum for mathematics

2. Knowledge of assessments for mathematics

3. Knowledge of instructional strategies for mathematics

4. Knowledge of student understanding of mathematics (Magnusson, Krajcik, and Borko 1999)

These four components are linked in significant ways to the content that you teach.

Even though it is important for you to consider how to structure lessons, deciding what group and class management techniques you will use, how you will allocate time, and what will be the general flow of the lesson, Shulman (1986) noted that it is even more important to consider *what* is taught and the *way* in which it is taught. Every day, you make at least five essential decisions as you determine—

1. which explanations to offer (or not);

2. which representations of the mathematics to use;

3. what types of questions to ask;

4. what depth to expect in responses from students to the questions posed; and

5. how to deal with students' misunderstandings when these become evident in their responses.

Your pedagogical content knowledge is the unique blending of your content expertise and your skill in pedagogy to create a knowledge base that allows you to make robust instructional decisions. Shulman (1986, p. 9) defined pedagogical content knowledge as "a second kind of content knowledge…, which goes beyond knowledge of the subject matter per se to the dimension of subject matter knowledge *for teaching*." He explained further:

> Pedagogical content knowledge also includes an understanding of what makes the learning of specific topics easy or difficult: the conceptions and preconceptions that students of different ages and backgrounds bring with them to the learning of those most frequently taught topics and lessons. (p. 9)

If you consider the five decision areas identified at the top of the page, you will note that each of these requires knowledge of the mathematical content and the associated pedagogy. For example, when students are classifying shapes, they must consider multiple perspectives to see relationships between and among them. Your knowledge of geometry and measurement can help you craft tasks and questions that provide counterexamples and ways to guide your students in seeing connections within and among the multiple aspects of geometry and measurement concepts. As you establish the content, complete with learning goals, you then need to consider how to move your students from their initial understandings to deeper ones, building rich connections along the way.

The instructional sequence that you design to meet student learning goals has to take into consideration the misconceptions and misunderstandings that you might expect to encounter (along with the strategies that you expect to use to negotiate them), your expectation of the level of difficulty of the topic for your students, the progression of experiences in which your students will engage, appropriate collections of representations for the content, and relationships between and among geometry, measurement, and other topics.

Model of Teacher Knowledge

Grossman (1990) extended Shulman's ideas to create a model of teacher knowledge with four domains (see fig. 0.1):

1. Subject-matter knowledge

2. General pedagogical knowledge

3. Pedagogical content knowledge

4. Knowledge of context

Subject-matter knowledge includes mathematical facts, concepts, rules, and relationships among concepts. Your understanding of the mathematics affects the way in which you teach the content—the ideas that you emphasize, the ones that you do not, particular algorithms that you use, and so on (Hill, Rowan, and Ball 2005).

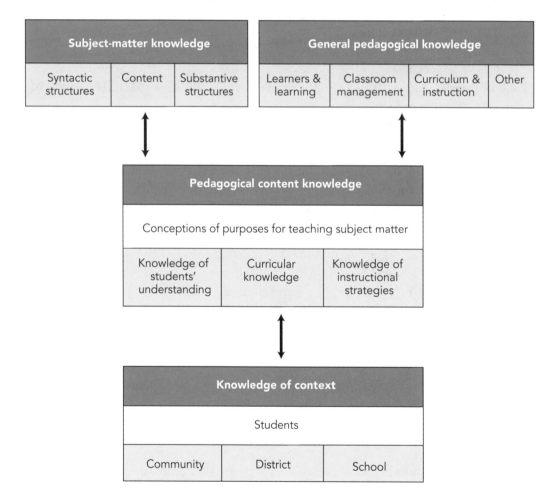

Fig. 0.1. Grossman's (1990, p. 5) model of teacher knowledge

Your pedagogical knowledge relates to the general knowledge, beliefs, and skills that you possess about instructional practices. These include specific instructional strategies that you use, the amount of wait time that you allow for students' responses to questions or tasks, classroom management techniques that you use for setting expectations and organizing students, and your grouping techniques, which might include having your students work individually or cooperatively or collaboratively, in groups or pairs. As Grossman's model indicates, your understanding and interpretation of the environment of your school, district, and community can also have an impact on the way in which you teach a topic.

Note that pedagogical content knowledge has four aspects, or components, in Grossman's (1990) model:

1. Conceptions of purposes for teaching

2. Knowledge of students' understanding

3. Knowledge of curriculum

4. Knowledge of instructional strategies

Each of these components has specific connections to the classroom. It is useful to consider each one in turn.

First, when you think about the goals that you want to establish for your instruction, you are focusing on your conceptions of the purposes for teaching. This is a broad category but an important one because the goals that you set will define learning outcomes for your students. These conceptions influence the other three components of pedagogical content knowledge. Hence, they appropriately occupy their overarching position in the model.

Second, your knowledge of your students' understanding of the mathematics content is central to good teaching. To know what your students understand, you must focus on both their conceptions and their misconceptions. As teachers, we all recognize that students develop naïve understandings that may or may not be immediately evident to us in their work or discourse. These can become deep-rooted misconceptions that are not simply errors that students make. Misconceptions may include incorrect generalizations that students have developed, such as thinking that area is defined as length times width. These generalizations may even be predictable notions that students exhibit as part of a developmental trajectory, as in moving from counting square units of area to developing formulas and more sophisticated means for determining area.

Part of your responsibility as a teacher is to present tasks or to ask questions that can bring misconceptions to the forefront. Once you become aware of misconceptions in students' thinking, you then have to determine the next instructional steps. The mathematical ideas presented in this volume focus on common misconceptions that students form in relation to specific, interrelated topics—geometry and measurement in grades 3–5. This book shows how the type of task selected and the sequencing of carefully developed questions can bring the misconceptions to light, as well as how particular teachers took the next instructional steps to challenge the students' misconceptions.

Third, curricular knowledge for mathematics includes multiple areas. Your teaching may be guided by a set of standards such as the Common Core State Standards for Mathematics (CCSSM; National Governors Association Center for Best Practices and Council of Chief State School Officers 2010) or other provincial, state, or local standards. You may in fact use these standards as the learning outcomes for your students. Your textbook is another source that may influence your instruction. With any textbook also comes a particular philosophical view of mathematics, mathematics teaching, and student learning. Your awareness and understanding of the curricular perspectives related to the choice of standards and the selection of a textbook can help to determine how you actually enact your curriculum. Moreover, your district or school may have a pacing guide that influences your delivery of the curriculum. In this book, we can focus only on the alignment of the topics presented with broader curricular perspectives, such as CCSSM. However, your own understanding of and expertise with your other curricular resources, coupled with the parameters defined by the expected student outcomes from standards documents, can provide the specificity that you need for your classroom.

In addition to your day-to-day instructional decisions, you make daily decisions about which tasks from curricular materials you can use without adaptation, which tasks you will need to adapt, and which tasks you will need to create on your own. Once you select or develop meaningful, high-quality tasks and use them in your mathematics lesson, you have launched what Yinger (1988) called "a three-way conversation between teacher, student, and problem" (p. 86). This process is not simple—it is complex because how students respond to the problem or task is directly linked to your next instructional move. That means that you have to plan multiple instructional paths to choose among as students respond to those tasks.

Knowledge of the curriculum goes beyond the curricular materials that you use. You also consider the mathematical knowledge that students bring with them from grade 2 and what they should learn by the end of grade 5. The way in which you teach a foundational concept or skill has an impact on the way in which students will interact with and learn later related content. For example, the types of representations that you include in your introduction of geometry and measurement are the ones that your students will use to evaluate other representations and ideas in later grades.

Fourth, knowledge of instructional strategies is essential to pedagogical content knowledge. Having a wide array of instructional strategies for teaching mathematics is central to effective teaching and learning. Instructional strategies, along with knowledge of the curriculum, may include the selection of mathematical tasks, together with the way in which those tasks will be enacted in the classroom. Instructional strategies may also include the way in which the mathematical content will be structured for students. You may have very specific ways of thinking about how you will structure your presentation of a mathematical idea—not only how you will sequence the introduction and development of the idea but also how you will present that idea to your students. Which examples should you select, and which questions should you ask? What representations should you use? Your knowledge of instructional strategies, coupled with your knowledge of your curriculum, permits you to align the selected mathematical tasks closely with the way in which your students perform those tasks in your classroom.

The instructional approach in this volume combines a student-centered perspective with an approach to mathematics through problem solving. A student-centered approach is characterized by a shared focus on student and teacher conversations, including interactions among students. Students who learn through such an approach are active in the learning process and develop ways of evaluating their own work and one another's in concert with the teacher's evaluation.

Teaching through problem solving makes tasks or problems the core of mathematics teaching and learning. The introduction to a new topic consists of a task that students work through, drawing on their previous knowledge while connecting it with new ideas. After students have explored the introductory task (or tasks), their consideration of solution methods, the uniqueness or multiplicity of solutions, and extensions of the task create rich opportunities for discussion and the development of specific mathematical concepts and skills.

By combining the two approaches, teachers create a dynamic, interactive, and engaging classroom environment for their students. This type of environment promotes the ability of students to demonstrate CCSSM's Standards for Mathematical Practice while learning the mathematics at a deep level.

The chapters that follow will show that instructional sequences embed all the characteristics of knowledge of instructional strategies that Grossman (1990) identifies. One component that is not explicit in Grossman's model but is included in a model developed by Magnusson, Krajcik, and Borko (1999) is the knowledge of assessment. Your knowledge of assessment in mathematics plays an important role in guiding your instructional decision-making process.

There are different types of assessments, each of which can influence the evidence that you collect as well as your view of what students know (or don't know) and how they know what they do. Your interpretation of what students know is also related to your view of what constitutes "knowing" in mathematics. As you examine the tasks, classroom vignettes, and samples of student work in this volume, you will notice that teacher questioning permits formative assessment that supplies information that spans both conceptual and procedural aspects of understanding. *Formative assessment,* as this book uses the term, refers to an appraisal that occurs during an instructional segment, with the aim of adjusting instruction to meet the needs of students more effectively (Popham 2006). Formative assessment does not always require a paper-and-pencil product but may include questions that you ask or tasks that students complete during class.

The information that you gain from student responses can provide you with feedback that guides the instructional flow, while giving you a sense of how deeply (or superficially) your students understand a particular idea—or whether they hold a misconception that is blocking their progress. As you monitor your students' development of rich understanding, you can continually compare their responses with your expectations and then adapt your instructional plans to accommodate their current levels of development. Wiliam (2007, p. 1054) described this interaction between teacher expectations and student performance in the following way:

> It is therefore about assessment functioning as a bridge between teaching and learning, helping teachers collect evidence about student achievement in order to adjust instruction to better meet student learning needs, in real time.

Wiliam notes that for teachers to get the best information about student understandings, they have to know how to facilitate substantive class discussions, choose tasks that include opportunities for students to demonstrate their learning, and employ robust and effective questioning strategies. From these strategies, you must then interpret student responses and scaffold their learning to help them progress to more complex ideas.

Characteristics of Tasks

The type of task that is presented to students is very important. Tasks that focus only on procedural aspects may not help students learn a mathematical idea deeply.

Superficial learning may result in students forgetting easily, requiring reteaching, and potentially affecting how they understand mathematical ideas that they encounter in the future. Thus, the tasks selected for inclusion in this volume emphasize deep learning of significant mathematical ideas. These rich, "high-quality" tasks have the power to create a foundation for more sophisticated ideas and support an understanding that goes beyond "how" to "why." Figure 0.2 identifies the characteristics of a high-quality task.

As you move through this volume, you will notice that it sequences tasks for each mathematical idea so that they provide a cohesive and connected approach to the identified concept. The tasks build on one another to ensure that each student's thinking becomes increasingly sophisticated, progressing from a novice's view of the content to a perspective that is closer to that of an expert. We hope that you will find the tasks useful in your own classes.

A high-quality task has the following characteristics:
Aligns with relevant mathematics content standard(s)
Encourages the use of multiple representations
Provides opportunities for students to develop and demonstrate the mathematical practices
Involves students in an inquiry-oriented or exploratory approach
Allows entry to the mathematics at a low level (all students can begin the task) but also has a high ceiling (some students can extend the activity to higher-level activities)
Connects previous knowledge to new learning
Allows for multiple solution approaches and strategies
Engages students in explaining the meaning of the result
Includes a relevant and interesting context

Fig. 0.2. Characteristics of a high-quality task

Types of Questions

The questions that you pose to your students in conjunction with a high-quality task may at times cause them to confront ideas that are at variance with or directly contradictory to their own beliefs. The state of mind that students then find themselves in is called *cognitive dissonance*, which is not a comfortable state for students–or, on occasion, for the teacher. The tasks in this book are structured in a way that forces students to deal with two conflicting ideas. However, it is through the process of negotiating the contradictions that students come to know the content much more deeply. How the teacher handles this negotiation determines student learning.

You can pose three types of questions to support your students' process of working with and sorting out conflicting ideas. These questions are characterized by their potential to encourage reversibility, flexibility, and generalization in students' thinking (Dougherty 2001). All three types of questions require more than a one-word or one-number answer. Reversibility questions are those that have the capacity to change the direction of students' thinking. They often give students the solution and require them to create the corresponding problem. A flexibility question can be one of two types: it can ask students to solve a problem in more than one way, or it can ask them to compare and contrast two or more problems or determine the relationship between or among concepts and skills. Generalization questions also come in two types: they ask students to look at multiple examples or cases and find a pattern or make observations, or they ask them to create a specific example of a rule, conjecture, or pattern. Figure 0.3 provides examples of reversibility, flexibility, and generalization questions related to geometry and measurement in grades 3–5.

Type of question	Example
Reversibility question	What rectangle(s) could have an area of 48 square units?
Flexibility question	What is the perimeter of a rectangle that measures 4 inches by 8 inches? Find the perimeter by using another method.
Flexibility question	What is the perimeter of a rectangle that measures 3 centimeters by 2 centimeters? What is the perimeter of a rectangle that measures 3 centimeters by 3 centimeters?
Generalization question	If you know the perimeter of a rectangle, can you predict the area of the rectangle? Why or why not?
Generalization question	What characteristics do all parallelograms have?

Fig. 0.3. Examples of reversibility, flexibility, and generalization questions

Conclusion

The Introduction has provided a brief overview of the nature of—and necessity for—pedagogical content knowledge. This knowledge, which you use in your classroom every day, is the indispensable medium through which you transmit your understanding of the big ideas of the mathematics to your students. It determines your selection of appropriate, high-quality tasks and enables you to ask the types of questions that will not only move your students forward in their understanding but also allow you to determine the depth of that understanding.

The chapters that follow describe important ideas related to learners, curricular goals, instructional strategies, and assessment that can assist you in transforming your students' knowledge into formal mathematical ideas related to geometry and measurement. These chapters provide specific examples of mathematical tasks and student thinking for you to analyze to develop your pedagogical content knowledge for teaching geometry and measurement in grades 3–5 or to give you ideas to help other colleagues develop this knowledge. You will also see how to bring together and interweave your knowledge of learners, curriculum, instructional strategies, and assessment to support your students in grasping the big ideas and essential understandings and using them to build more sophisticated knowledge.

Before students reach grades 3–5, they have already had many experiences that affect their initial understanding of geometry and measurement and have developed some ideas about these topics. Students in pre-K–grade 2 classrooms frequently demonstrate understanding of mathematical ideas related to geometry and measurement in a particular context or in connection with related topics. Yet, in other situations, these same students do not demonstrate that same understanding. As their teacher in grades 3–5, you must understand the ideas that they have developed about geometry and measurement in their previous experiences so you can extend their knowledge and see whether or how it differs from the formal mathematical knowledge that they need to be successful in reasoning with or applying these ideas. You have the important responsibility of assessing their current knowledge related to the big ideas of geometry and measurement as well as their understanding of various representations of these ideas and their power and limitations. Your understanding will facilitate and reinforce your instructional decisions. Teaching the big mathematical ideas and helping students develop essential understandings related to geometry and measurement are obviously very challenging and complex tasks.

into practice

Chapter 1
Reasoning with Two-Dimensional Shapes and Their Attributes

Big Idea 3
A classification scheme specifies the properties of objects that are relevant to particular goals and intentions.

Students begin to form ideas about geometric shapes and their attributes in kindergarten–grade 2—and even earlier—both inside and outside the classroom. For example, they see and hear about triangles, squares, and rectangles in a variety of children's books, and they use common shapes in board games and video games. They draw squares with triangles "on top" to represent houses in two dimensions, and they build 3-D houses with blocks in early, hands-on experiences with cubes and other solids. They encounter and manipulate spheres when they play with balls, and they see circles everywhere—in the shapes of plates, traffic lights, and wheels on cars and trucks.

An important part of your task as a teacher in grades 3–5 is to uncover the meanings that your students have constructed for these shapes so that you can extend and build on them, correcting or modifying them as necessary, to nurture the mathematical knowledge that they need to work with geometric shapes and their attributes successfully in the upper elementary years and beyond, as they advance in mathematics. Assessing your students' current knowledge is essential to the instructional decisions that you make as you work to deepen their understanding of geometric shapes and strengthen and clarify their understanding of the power and limitations of various representations of these shapes and their attributes.

Building Understanding of Geometric Properties: Working toward Big Idea 3

To help your students build robust understanding of geometric shapes, attributes, and properties, you must—

- design, adapt, or select worthwhile mathematical tasks;

- interpret the responses of individual students; and

- make instructional decisions based on the results of your work.

These critical practices require specialized knowledge. For example, analyze the Triangle task and the Rectangle task in figure 1.1, using the questions posed in Reflect 1.1 as guides.

Reflect 1.1

Figure 1.1 shows tasks that focus students' attention on triangles and rectangles. How do you think your students would respond to these tasks?

What wrong answers would you anticipate as likely?

Why might students come up with those wrong answers?

What are the benefits of using tasks that require students to compare and contrast shapes?

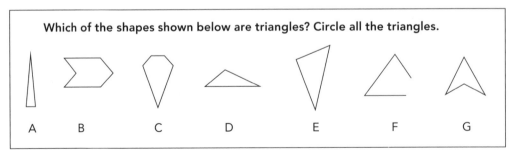

Which of the shapes shown below are triangles? Circle all the triangles.

A   B   C   D   E   F   G

Fig. 1.1. Triangle task and Rectangle task: Distinguishing triangles and rectangles from other shapes

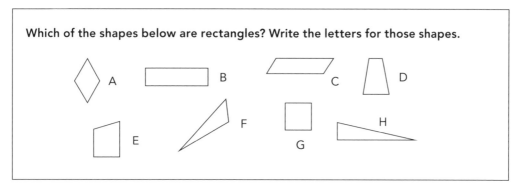

Which of the shapes below are rectangles? Write the letters for those shapes.

Fig. 1.1. *Continued*

As children work with shapes, they often focus on their general appearance. When students do not have experiences with varied examples of shapes, they often form misconceptions about specific shapes—perhaps thinking that only equilateral triangles are triangles, for example. Clements and Sarama (2009) argue, "Children can learn richer concepts about shape if their educational environment includes four features: varied examples and non-examples, discussions about shapes and their attributes, a wider variety of shape classes, and a broad array of geometric tasks" (p. 133). To gain further insight into the different ways that students may view triangles and rectangles, we posed the Triangle task in figure 1.1 to 95 students who had nearly completed grade 3, 4, or 5. Almost all the fourth- and fifth-grade students (that is, 95 percent in both grades) answered correctly. Of the 39 third graders in our sample, 30 students (about 77 percent) answered correctly. Consider the understandings and misunderstandings demonstrated by third-grade students in the samples of work shown in figures 1.2–1.4. As you review the students' responses, refer to the questions in Reflect 1.2.

Reflect 1.2

Figures 1.2–1.4 show responses from three third graders to the Triangle task in figure 1.1. How would you characterize the mathematical understandings and misunderstandings that these students exhibit?

What specific strategies would you use or questions would you pose to move these students forward?

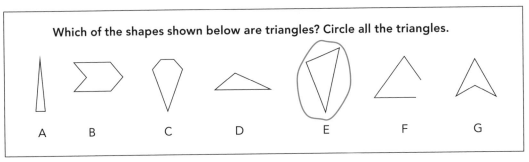

Fig. 1.2. Alison's (grade 3) response to the Triangle task in figure 1.1

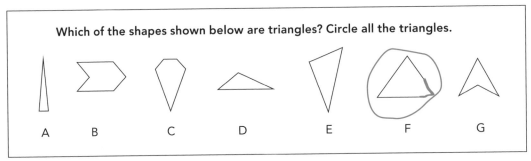

Fig. 1.3. Patrick's (grade 3) response to the Triangle task in figure 1.1

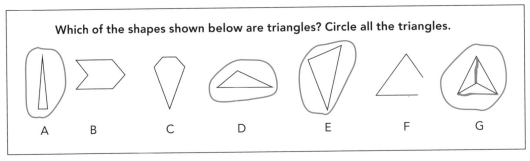

Fig. 1.4. Angelina's (grade 3) response to the Triangle task in figure 1.1

Pierre M. van Hiele and Dina van Hiele-Geldof (1958) introduced a framework that identifies five levels of cognitive development in geometry (see Clements and Battista [1992] for a more detailed description). At level 1 (Visual), students identify, name, and compare geometric features (triangles and rectangles, for example) according to their appearance. For example, a student might say, "Both of those figures are triangles because they look the same" (Fuys, Geddes, and Tischler 1988). In the Triangle task presented in figure 1.1, Alison, the third-grade student whose work is shown in figure 1.2, selected only shape E, whereas Patrick, whose work is shown in figure 1.3, selected only shape F—after extending the sides. Patrick may have ignored shapes A, D, and E because they did not "fit" his image of a triangle. Both Patrick and Alison demonstrated level 1 thinking in relation to triangles. Triangles apparently had to have a specific shape and orientation to "fit" their notions of triangle. Angelina, whose work appears in figure 1.4, selected not only shapes A, D, and E but also—after adding a couple of lines—shape G. In fact, 7 of the 39 third graders included G (the chevron) in their selection of triangles. However, Angelina's case is noteworthy because she drew two additional lines before she decided it was a triangle. In such a case, posing follow-up questions would be helpful: "Why did you choose shape G as a triangle, Angelina?" "Why did you draw these additional lines?"

For students in grades 3–5, focusing on attributes is important. Noting that triangles have three straight sides (connected at their endpoints) helps students move away from a focus on general appearance to a focus on properties. Students have developed mental images of triangles and associated properties that match their experiences. For example, many students identify as triangles only those shapes that have a side parallel to the bottom of the page on which they appear, or those with a "point" at the "top," or those with all sides the same length. Adults and children alike often refer to mental images and the properties that they associate with an object when thinking about, creating, or evaluating a representation of that object. Tall and Vinner (1981) refer to this as a "concept image."

If you find that you have students who have developed a concept image of a triangle that requires that all triangles have a point on top, then you need to design tasks and instruction that will address that faulty concept image. You must place consistent emphasis on the definition of a triangle as having three (straight) sides and give your students opportunities to consider examples such as shape E in figure 1.1, which is a triangle that does not have a "pointy top."

To gain further insight into the different ways that students may view basic shapes, we designed the Rectangle task also shown in figure 1.1, reproduced here as figure 1.5. We gave this task to 127 students who had nearly completed grade 3, 4, or 5.

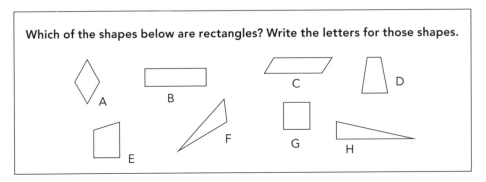

Which of the shapes below are rectangles? Write the letters for those shapes.

Fig. 1.5. Rectangle task, reproduced from figure 1.1

The Rectangle task elicited a wider variety of answers than the Triangle task; figure 1.6 shows the outcome. Examine these results, and respond to the questions in Reflect 1.3 to probe deeper into the students' responses to this task.

Grade	Students choosing only shape B	Students choosing shapes B and C	Students choosing shapes B and G	Students choosing shapes B, C, and G	Other
3 (43 students)	16 (37%)	17 (40%)	4 (9%)	2 (5%)	4 (9%)
4 (35 students)	10 (29%)	5 (14%)	15 (43%)	2 (6%)	3 (9%)
5 (49 students)	16 (33%)	2 (4%)	31 (63%)	0	0
Total (127 students)	42 (33%)	24 (19%)	50 (39%)	4 (3%)	7 (6%)

Fig. 1.6. Students' responses by grade level to the Rectangle task

Reflect 1.3

Examine the shapes presented in the Rectangle task in figure 1.5. How would you characterize the mathematical understandings and misunderstandings of the students who selected only shape B as a rectangle?

How would you characterize the mathematical understandings and misunderstandings of the students who selected shapes B and C?

Reflect 1.3, *continued*

How would you characterize the mathematical understandings and misunderstandings of the students who selected shapes B, C, and G?

What specific strategies would you use or questions would you pose to move these various students forward in their understanding?

Providing your students with opportunities to examine examples and non-examples of specific shapes, followed by opportunities to participate in a facilitated discussion (or debate), will challenge their conceptions of the shapes. You can offer such opportunities through tasks that—

- involve images (such as the Rectangle task in fig. 1.5);

- require students to sort shapes; or

- require students to identify shapes in real-world settings (for example, the classroom) or pictures (from magazines, for instance).

Through these types of activities, you can determine which students are focusing only on the appearance and the mental or visual image of the shape (van Hiele level 1: Visual) and which students are analyzing figures in terms of their attributes and properties (van Hiele level 2: Descriptive/Analytic).

To help teachers distinguish student responses according to these two levels, Fuys, Geddes, and Tischler (1988, pp. 58–63) created tables that provide sample responses for each level. These examples can not only help you assess your students' responses in relation to the van Hiele levels of geometric development but also guide you as you select and design tasks and discussion questions. Figures 1.7 and 1.8 provide excerpts of Fuys, Geddes, and Tischler's tables for the first two levels. Compare and contrast the tables, and then respond to the questions in Reflect 1.4.

Level 1 descriptors *The student—*	Sample student responses

1. identifies instances of a shape by its appearance as a whole—
  a. in a simple drawing, diagram, or set of cutouts;
  b. in different positions;
  c. in a shape or other more complex configurations.
	Student identifies squares in a set of cutout shapes or drawings.
	Student points out angles, rectangles, and triangles in different positions in a photograph or on a page of diagrams.
	Student points to the right angles in a right trapezoid.

2. constructs, draws, or copies a shape.	Student makes figures (e.g., rectangles) with sticks. Student makes a tiling pattern with cutout triangles and copies the pattern on paper.
3. names or labels shapes and other geometric configurations and uses standard and/or nonstandard names and labels appropriately.	Student refers to a square as a diamond. Student refers to angles by color (e.g., the red angle) or by letter symbols (e.g., angle *A*).
4. compares and sorts shapes on the basis of their appearance as a whole.	Student says, "One is a square; the other is a rectangle," or responds, "One is wider," when asked to say what is different about a square and rectangle. Student sorts quadrilaterals into "squares, rectangles, and others" because "they look alike."
5. describes shapes verbally by their appearance as a whole.	Student describes a rectangle by saying that it "looks like a square" or a parallelogram as "a slanty rectangle."
6. solves routine problems by operating on shapes rather than by using properties that apply in general.	Student verifies that opposite sides of a rectangle are parallel by placing sticks on its edges.

7. identifies parts of a figure, but—
  a. does *not* analyze a figure in terms of its components;
  b. does *not* think of properties as characterizing a class of figures;
  c. does *not* make generalizations about shapes or use related language.
	Student identifies squares by appearance but does *not* introduce "equal sides and right angles" or "square corners."
	Student points to sides of a square and measures to check that they are equal but does *not* generalize equal sides for all squares.
	Student does *not* use "all," "some," "every," "none," or any other such quantifier to say whether all, some, or none of a certain type of shape have a property.

Fig. 1.7. Descriptors for van Hiele level 1 (Visual) and sample student responses. Adapted from Fuys, Geddes, and Tischler (1988, pp. 58–59).

Level 2 descriptors *The student—*	Sample student responses
1. identifies and tests relationships among components of figures.	Student points to sides and angles of a figure and notes, "It has 4 right angles, and all 4 sides are equal."
2. recalls and uses appropriate vocabulary for components and relationships.	Student observes that for a parallelogram, "These opposite sides are parallel, and so are these," checking with sticks that the sides do not meet or are equally spaced.
3 a. compares two shapes according to relationships among their components. b. sorts shapes in different ways according to certain properties, including a sorting of all instances of a class from non-instances.	Student tells how a cutout square and rectangle are alike and different in terms of their angles and sides. Student makes up a rule for sorting quadrilaterals (e.g., according to the number of right angles or by the number of pairs of parallel sides).
4. interprets and uses verbal description of a figure in relation to its properties and uses this description to draw or construct the figure.	Student reads on property cards "4 sides" and "all sides equal" and tries to draw a shape that has these two properties but is not a square.
5. discovers properties of specific figures empirically and generalizes properties for that class of figures.	After several instances of putting two congruent right triangles together to form a rectangle, student says, "You can find the area of a right triangle by making a rectangle and taking half its area."
6. a. describes a class of figures (e.g., parallelograms) in terms of its properties. b. tells what shape a figure is, given certain properties.	Student describes a square over the telephone to a friend, saying, "It has 4 sides, 4 right angles, all sides are equal, and opposite sides are parallel." Given certain properties as clues about a shape, student tells what shape it must be on the basis of the properties.
7. identifies which properties used to characterize one class of figures also apply to another class of figures and compares classes of figures according to their properties.	Having noted that parallelograms have "opposite sides parallel," student adds, "Oh, so do squares and rectangles."
8. discovers properties of an unfamiliar class of figures.	After completing a sorting of quadrilaterals into kites and non-kites, student discovers and verbalizes properties that characterize kites.
9. solves geometric problems by using known properties of figures or by insightful approaches.	Student figures out how to find the area of a new shape by subdividing or transforming it into shapes whose areas he or she can already determine (e.g., a parallelogram into 2 triangles and a rectangle or into a rectangle).
10. formulates and uses generalizations about properties of figures and uses related language, but— a. does *not* explain how certain properties of a figure are interrelated; b. does *not* formulate and use formal definitions; c. does *not* explain subclass relationships beyond checking specific instances against given list of properties; d. does *not* see a need for proof or logical explanations of generalizations discovered empirically, and does *not* use related language correctly.	When asked to define a parallelogram, student lists many properties but does not identify a set of necessary or a set of sufficient properties. After listing the properties of all the members of the quadrilateral family, student cannot explain why "all rectangles are parallelograms" or why "all squares are kites."

Fig. 1.8. Descriptors for van Hiele level 2 (Descriptive/Analytic) and sample student responses. Adapted from Fuys, Geddes, and Tischler (1988, pp. 60–63).

Reflect 1.4

How do van Hiele levels 1 and 2 differ?

In what ways could you use the tables in figures 1.7 and 1.8 to plan your instruction related to geometric shapes?

In what ways could you use these tables as a rubric to assess your students?

We asked students to complete a second rectangle task in addition to the earlier task that asked them simply to identify the rectangles in a set of shapes. Work on the Write about Rectangles task, shown in figure 1.9, can provide further insight into the properties that students attend to as they consider what makes a rectangle a rectangle. Examine this task, and then respond to the questions in Reflect 1.5.

Write down everything that is true about all rectangles.

Fig. 1.9. Write about Rectangles task

Reflect 1.5

Which attributes and properties of rectangles would you expect students in grades 3, 4, and 5 to include in responses to the Write about Rectangles task in figure 1.9?

How would you expect students' responses to differ by grade level?

Students in grades 3–5 who completed this second task typically wrote two or three statements. The most common statements are listed in figure 1.10. Note that not all these responses are correct. Analyze the responses in the figure, guided by the questions in Reflect 1.6.

Reflect 1.6

Figure 1.10 shows statements from students in response to the Write about Rectangles task in figure 1.9. Which of these statements are actually true for all rectangles?

How might you help the students who made these statements begin to analyze a shape in terms of its components?

Sample student responses to the Write about Rectangles task in figure 1.9

- Rectangles have 4 sides.
- Rectangles have 4 right angles.
- Rectangles are quadrilaterals.
- Rectangles have 2 long sides and 2 short sides.
- Rectangles are polygons.
- Opposite sides have the same length.
- Opposite sides are parallel.

Fig. 1.10. Students' statements of what is true of all rectangles

The attributes of a rectangle that students in grades 3–5 focused on primarily were the number of sides and the relationships between opposite sides. Although students recognized that the opposite sides of rectangles are the same length, a common misconception was that all sides of a rectangle should not be the same length. Figure 1.11 shows work from a third-grade student illustrating the belief that a rectangle necessarily has "two long sides and two short sides." We noted that some students in grades 4 and 5 also held this misconception.

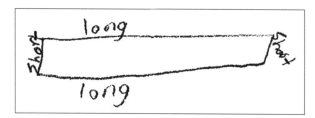

Fig. 1.11. Work showing a third-grade student's misconception that all rectangles have two long sides and two short sides

Students appeared for the most part to have a van Hiele level 2 understanding of rectangles in relation to the Write about Rectangles task in figure 1.9. They typically formulated generalizations about rectangles but did not explain how certain properties of a figure were related. For example, 27 students out of 132 stated that a rectangle has four sides and four vertices, but they did not demonstrate an understanding of the fact that in a polygon the numbers of sides and vertices are necessarily the same. Many students did not show that they understood subclass relationships, although some students (mainly in fifth grade) wrote that a rectangle can be a square.

In contrast to the typical responses, a few students focused on the appearance of the figure, indicating a van Hiele level 1 understanding. Consider the following statements from three third-grade students:

- "All rectangles can be long. They can be standing up."

- "Sometimes rectangles can be right side up or looking down."

- "The rectangle is a long square. It has 4 sides and 4 right angles. It could turn any way."

An analysis of the students' work on the Triangle, Rectangle, and Write about Rectangles tasks discussed previously revealed that some students had specific conceptions (or misconceptions) about what rectangles and triangles "looked like" (van Hiele level 1). To investigate the influence of the orientation of a shape on students' thinking more closely, we gave 39 third-grade students the task in figure 1.12, Is It a Square? Examine this task, guided by the questions in Reflect 1.7.

Reflect 1.7

How would you anticipate that your students would respond to the task Is It a Square? shown in figure 1.12?

What wrong answers would you anticipate?

Why would you expect students to give those wrong answers?

What specific strategies would you use or questions would you pose to move these students forward?

What do you see as the benefits of using tasks that orient shapes in atypical ways?

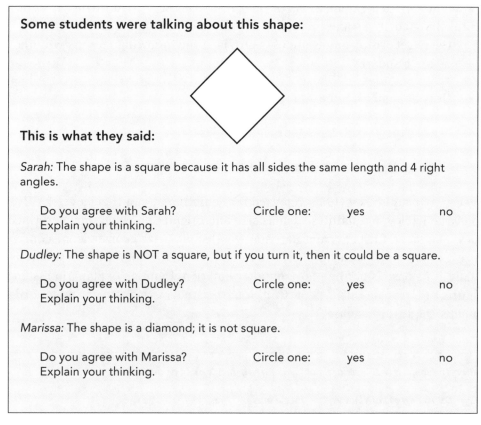

Some students were talking about this shape:

This is what they said:

Sarah: The shape is a square because it has all sides the same length and 4 right angles.

> Do you agree with Sarah?   Circle one: yes   no
> Explain your thinking.

Dudley: The shape is NOT a square, but if you turn it, then it could be a square.

> Do you agree with Dudley?   Circle one: yes   no
> Explain your thinking.

Marissa: The shape is a diamond; it is not square.

> Do you agree with Marissa?   Circle one: yes   no
> Explain your thinking.

Fig. 1.12. Is It a Square? A task designed to give insight into students' views on the orientation of a square

Of the 39 third graders, 35 students answered the three yes-no questions in the task in seven different ways. The other 4 students left one item blank or responded with "kinda." The three most popular responses from third-grade students are displayed in figure 1.13. The shaded row in the figure highlights the correct answer. (A small percentage [23%] of third-grade students answered all three questions correctly.)

Response	Number of third graders
Disagreed with Sarah, but agreed with Dudley and Marissa	11 (28%)
Agreed with Sarah and Dudley, but disagreed with Marissa	9 (23%)
Agreed with Sarah, but disagreed with Dudley and Marissa	9 (23%)

Fig. 1.13. The three most popular responses from third graders to the task Is It a Square? shown in figure 1.12

The students' written explanations of their responses permitted further insight into their thinking about a square with a "different" orientation (no side parallel to the edge of the page). Third-grade students provided the following reasons why the shape was not a square:

- "It is a rhombus, not a square."

- "The shape doesn't have four right angles."

- "If you turn it, it will be a square."

Burger and Shaughnessy (1986) reported that children at van Hiele level 1 (Visual) attended to irrelevant qualities such as size and orientation when they described shapes. Moreover, Clements and Battista (1992) summarize geometric misconceptions examined in the research literature and include the notion that a square is not a square if its base is not in a horizontal orientation. Dennis's explanation, shown in figure 1.14, reveals this type of thinking; the student was attempting to write "rhombus is a turned square."

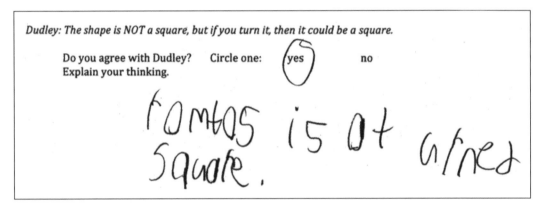

Fig. 1.14. Dennis's (grade 3) explanation of his agreement with Dudley's conclusion: "rhombus is a turned square"

Students at level 1 attend to attributes that are irrelevant. Therefore, using tasks that highlight attributes such as orientation and confront these misconceptions is critical as children continue to work with shapes through the use of manipulatives and computer software as well as representations on paper. Using shape sets that demonstrate a variety of examples is also helpful. If children's experiences with shapes are limited to pattern blocks, they may make assumptions that all triangles look like the green equilateral triangle block or all trapezoids look like the red block. Moreover, you must help your students connect physical models with representations of shapes on paper. How might Dennis have responded if he had been given a square object or a cutout square, asked to turn it, and then asked whether the shape had changed when he turned it? What if he had been asked to glue different square cutouts or trace them on the paper so that they showed different orientations? A response from Dennis based on work with manipulatives might have been different from his response shown in figure 1.14 to the thinking in Is It a Square? Providing opportunities for students to work with different tools and devoting sufficient attention to orientation are important in teaching lessons about geometric shapes in grades 3–5. These experiences will prepare students to reason with shapes and their attributes, a goal set out in the Common Core State Standards (National Governors Association Center for Best Practices and Council of Chief State School Officers), as shown in figure 1.15.

Common Core State Standards for Mathematics, Grade 3

Geometry

Reason with shapes and their attributes.

1. Understand that shapes in different categories (e.g., rhombuses, rectangles, and others) may share attributes (e.g., having four sides), and that the shared attributes can define a larger category (e.g., quadrilaterals). Recognize rhombuses, rectangles, and squares as examples of quadrilaterals, and draw examples of quadrilaterals that do not belong to any of these subcategories.

Fig. 1.15. Reason with shapes and their attributes.
CCSSM 3.G.1 (NGA Center and CCSSO 2010, p. 26).

Summarizing Pedagogical Content Knowledge to Support Big Idea 3

Teaching the mathematical ideas discussed in this chapter requires specialized knowledge related to the four components presented in the Introduction: learners, curriculum, instructional strategies, and assessment. The four sections that follow summarize some examples of these specialized knowledge bases in relation to Big Idea 3. Although we separate them to highlight their importance, we also recognize that they are connected and support one another.

Knowledge of learners

When students are given the opportunity to make sense of problems, they typically approach problem-solving situations in more than one way. Knowledge of learners involves anticipating possible student responses. However, on some occasions, you will encounter student thinking that is unique or unanticipated. Collecting different student approaches to mathematics problems over time can help in planning for future instruction. The van Hiele (1958, 1959, 1986) framework helps in understanding students' cognitive development in relation to geometric shapes and their attributes. In addition, Fuys, Geddes, and Tischler's (1988) correlations of descriptors for levels 1 and 2 with sample student responses, shown in figures 1.7 and 1.8, provide helpful examples that illustrate how the van Hiele framework often manifests itself in the thinking of students in grades 3–5. These examples can help you anticipate responses of your students and plan your own responses to them.

Knowledge of curriculum

As stated earlier, Clements and Sarama (2009) argue, "Children can learn richer concepts about shape if their educational environment includes four features: varied examples and non-examples, discussions about shapes and their attributes, a wider variety of shape classes, and a broad array of geometric tasks" (p. 133). Therefore, the selection of the examples and non-examples is critical. As the samples of student work in this chapter suggest, students may experience many examples of rectangles that look like "two squares put together," as they might say or think, but they may not have many experiences with rectangles with different shapes or orientations (see Schifter [1999] for further discussion of this idea). How do the lessons in your curricular materials help students build an understanding of the meaning of geometric shapes? Do your materials vary the examples and non-examples that they include?

Knowledge of instructional strategies

Teachers have a multitude of instructional strategies to draw on when addressing geometric shapes and their attributes. This section highlights a few of these. One strategy is to encourage students to make comparisons and connections. Fosnot and Dolk (2002) suggest that students should wonder, ask questions such as "Why?" and "What if?" and notice patterns. Facilitating a whole-class discussion in which the students compare and contrast shapes such as those shown in figure 1.1 will generate interesting ideas and questions from them. Mack (2007) also provides a template for thirty-two shape cards that can be helpful for children to sort and compare.

Another instructional strategy that this chapter has illustrated involves having students analyze responses from fictitious students. Figure 1.12 shows a task (Is It a Square?) that asks students to agree or disagree with conjectures from fictitious children. Again, this strategy can lead to interesting whole-class discussions. In this case, the fictitious conjectures involve common misconceptions that teachers in grades 3–5 are likely to encounter. Rather than introducing a misconception through an examination of the work of a student in your own classroom, you can highlight the same idea and initiate a discussion of it through an examination of the work of "other students." Your students can then justify their reasoning for their agreement or disagreement with the work or thinking shown.

Knowledge of assessment

As noted in the Introduction to this book, Wiliam (2007) emphasizes the importance of selecting tasks that provide opportunities for students to demonstrate their thinking and for teachers to make instructional decisions. The work that students generated in response to the tasks discussed in this chapter provides evidence about their understandings and misunderstandings. The tasks asked students to explain their thinking, giving their teachers evidence to use in making determinations about future instruction. A yes-no or multiple-choice format provides information about correct and incorrect responses. However, requiring students to give a rationale for their choices gives teachers additional information about what the students understand. Yet, in many cases these explanations are insufficient or vague. In such cases, another assessment strategy would involve a variety of possible follow-up questions:

- "Why did you select that response?"

- "Why is Marissa's response incorrect?"

- "What information did you use to determine your answer?"

This strategy may serve multiple purposes, including moving the students' understanding forward, challenging an identified misconception, or allowing you to collect additional assessment information.

Conclusion

As Lehrer and Slovin (2014) discuss in connection with Big Idea 3 in *Developing Essential Understanding of Geometry and Measurement for Teaching Mathematics in Grades 3–5*, helping students develop essential understanding of the properties of shapes is critical. Yet, many students struggle to develop a deep understanding of geometric shapes and their attributes. Therefore, explicitly identifying the different attributes of shapes and comparing them during instruction are helpful. Developing these essential understandings requires a careful selection of tasks and effective questions. Chapter 2 continues this conversation by examining children's thinking in relation to another important attribute—angle.

practice

Chapter 2
Defining, Measuring, and Classifying Angles

Essential Understanding 2a
Measurement can specify "how much" by assigning a number that corresponds to a chosen unit to such attributes as length, area, volume, and angle.

Concepts of angle and rotation are critical to the development of geometric understanding (Clements and Battista 1992; Clements and Burns 2000). Yet, these concepts are challenging to teach and learn. Unfortunately, mathematics curricula do not typically devote sufficient time to support students' understanding of angle. Too often, instruction related to angles is limited to naming the different types of angles or measuring angles with protractors. This chapter highlights different definitions and interpretations of angles. It also emphasizes the unit of measure—degree—typically associated with angles, since degrees are quite different from other attributes that students in grades 3–5 have used to measure up to this point.

Thinking More Precisely about Angles: Working toward Essential Understanding 2a

To demonstrate some of the complexity and challenge involved in developing students' understanding of angle, we draw on the work of Keiser, Klee, and Fitch (2003), who gave 78 sixth-grade students the following task:

> Write a definition of ANGLE in your own words. Make it as complete as possible. You may use more than one or two sentences. (p. 116)

The definitions that the students gave in response to this task highlight ideas that they may have developed in grades 3–6. Figure 2.1 displays the results and provides examples of each emphasis. Analyze the data, and then complete Reflect 2.1.

Emphasis of definition	Sample response	Number of students with this emphasis (78 total students)	%
The degrees or the measure itself	"An angle is the number of degrees in a corner."	23	29.5%
The line segments that meet	"An angle is where two line segments intersect to form an angle."	20	25.6%
The opening	"How big apart the two lines are apart where the vertex is."	6	7.7%
The point	"An angle is where two vertices meet and make a point."	6	7.7%
The measure of the edge	"An angle is the measure of one side of a shape."	4	5.1%
A combination of two of these	"I think an angle is the measure in degrees between two line segments that are touching."	8	10.3%
Vague or wrong statements	"An angle is a shape that has straight lines and at least 3 angles."	11	14.1%

Fig. 2.1. Sixth-grade students' definitions of angles.
Adapted from Keiser, Klee, and Fitch (2003, p. 117).

Reflect 1.1

Figure 2.1 shows definitions of *angle* offered by sixth graders (Keiser, Klee, and Fitch 2003). What attributes did these sixth-grade students attend to as they wrote their definitions?

If your students gave these definitions, how would you use them to start a discussion about angles?

As demonstrated by the definitions in the table, students develop different meanings for the term *angle,* including a number of meanings that focus on points or line segments, without clear reference to how two segments or rays intersect, and these meanings therefore differ from formal definitions introduced during instruction. Driscoll (2007, p. 84) characterizes the definitions that students typically encounter, citing Keiser (2004) about their frequency:

> Definitions that students encounter often focus on one of the following ideas: (1) the union of two rays with a common endpoint (static), (2) the region contained between the two rays (static), or (3) the turning of a ray about a point from one position to another (dynamic). The first two are much more common than the third (Keiser 2004).

Students often interpret static representations of angles, such as the intersection of roads on a map, as different from dynamic representations, such as opening a door or turning a knob. Suggesting that student misconceptions related to angles may be associated with static representations of angle, Driscoll recommends that students have more exposure to dynamic representations.

Moreover, Mitchelmore (1998) argues that students may have difficulty coordinating the various dynamic views of angles as actions of turning and bending. He elaborates on this point: "Most young students may have a clear intuitive concept of turning about a point, but many do not spontaneously conceptualize it as a relation between two lines through a point" (p. 280). As you design instruction and assess your students' understandings and misunderstandings, you should carefully consider these different perspectives as well as the mathematical tasks, physical models, language, and representations that you will use with students in grades 3–5.

Mitchelmore offers some guidance (1998):

> It may be most effective to commence instruction in angle by examining such situations as scissors, fans, road junctions, furniture corners, and wall intersections in which the two arms of the angle are obvious. It should be relatively easy (compared to an introduction through turning or bending) for young students to develop simple concrete models, language, and drawing conventions that would allow them to compare and record a wide variety of angles in the environment. (p. 281)

These various physical contexts of angles may be thought of as examples of a standard angle concept, which Mitchelmore and White (2000) define as "two lines [or linear objects] meeting at a point and their relative inclination" (p. 217). Longitudinal studies of elementary school students have shown that students need considerable time to develop this standard concept of angle (Lehrer, Jenkins, and Osana 1998; Mitchelmore and White 2000). Keiser, Klee, and Fitch (2003) found that about

30 percent of the sixth graders in their study confused the definition of an angle with the measure of the angle (see the first row in the table in fig. 2.1).

To help your students understand the difference between an angle and its measure, you must give them opportunities to compare the sizes of angles without focusing on the angles' specific measures. For example, when students are comparing two angles such as *E* and *F* in figure 2.2, can they determine which angle is larger?

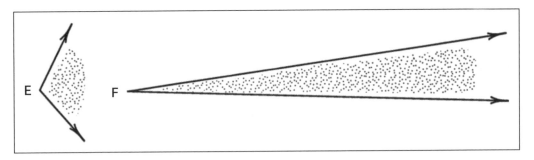

Fig. 2.2. Comparing the sizes of angles to determine which is larger.
From Page, Wagreich, and Chval (1993a, p. 4).

Van de Walle, Karp, and Bay-Williams (2010) refer to the attribute of angle size as the "spread of the angle's rays" (p. 386). Therefore, the measure of one angle is greater than another if its rays are "more open" (Munier, Devichi, and Merle 2008). Many students do not initially have this conception of angle size but attend to other features instead. One common misconception is that the size of the angle depends on the length of the rays, or angle sides, drawn in a diagram (Close 1982; Foxman and Ruddock 1984; Lehrer, Jenkins, and Osana 1998). Furthermore, Keiser, Klee, and Fitch (2003) reported that 76 percent of the sixth graders in their study agreed that the angle drawn on a map in their books would be smaller than the "scaled up" version in real life. Confronted with the angles in figure 2.2, students who hold these misconceptions might state that angle *F* is larger than angle *E*.

Such common objects as the hands on a clock face, scissor blades, pipe cleaners, and straws (either bendable or connected end to end with a paper clip) may be help-ful tools as students compare angles. For example, you might determine whether your students consider the angle on your watch to be the same as the angle on the clock on the classroom wall when both report 3:00. Or whether they focus on the amount of opening rather than the lengths of the blades when you create the same angle with the blades of small manicure scissors as with the blades of much larger classroom scissors. Or whether, in comparing the angles shown in figure 2.3, they are able to determine that angle *V* is the smallest.

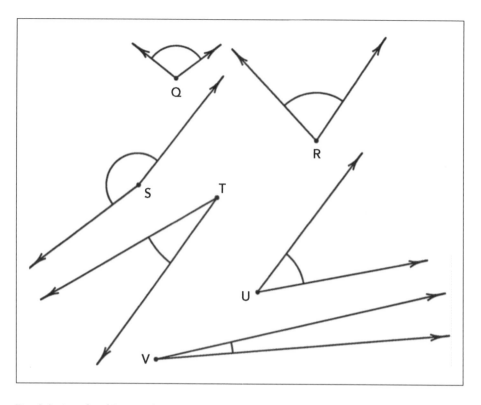

Fig. 2.3. A task asking students to compare angles to determine which is the smallest. From Page, Wagreich, and Chval (1993a, p. 18).

Measuring angles

Once students understand the attribute of angle size, they are ready to measure angles. As in the case of attributes such as length or area, beginning with a non-standard unit is beneficial. A standard unit for measuring angles is a degree, but not many students (or adults) have worked with angles that measure 1 degree (de-noted 1°). When students are learning to use standard units for measuring length, teachers may give them visual examples of things that measure 1 foot, 1 inch, 1 meter, or 1 centimeter in length. By analogy, showing students an angle that measures 1 degree might be helpful to them (Page, Wagreich, and Chval 1993a). Figure 2.4 shows such an angle. Notice that it is a very small angle; 90 of these are required to make a right angle, and 360 are needed to make a complete circle. The Common Core State Standards for Mathematics (National Governors Association Center for Best Practices and Council of Chief State School Officers [NGA Center and CCSSO] 2010) recommend that students in grade 4 have the opportunity to ex-plore this small unit of measure as a fraction of a circular arc and then iterate this unit to measure angles (see fig. 2.5).

Fig. 2.4. An angle with a measure of 1 degree

Common Core State Standards for Mathematics, Grade 4

Geometric measurement: understand concepts of angle and measure angles.

5. Recognize angles as geometric shapes that are formed wherever two rays share a common endpoint, and understand concepts of angle measurement:

    a. An angle is measured with reference to a circle with its center at the common endpoint of the rays, by considering the fraction of the circular arc between the points where the two rays intersect the circle. An angle that turns through 1/360 of a circle is called a "one-degree angle," and can be used to measure angles.

    b. An angle that turns through *n* one-degree angles is said to have an angle measure of *n* degrees.

Fig. 2.5. An angle is measured with reference to a circle.
Measurement and Data, CCSSM 4.MD.5a, 5b (NGA Center and CCSSO 2010, p. 31).

To help students understand the concept of angle measurement, Wilson and Adams (1992) suggest first using a nonstandard unit rather than a degree. By repeatedly folding and cutting a circle, students can create a "unit angle" that they may then use to measure other angles. Figure 2.6 illustrates a process for making one kind of unit angle.

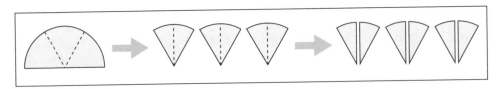

Fig. 2.6. Creating a wedge to measure angles with a nonstandard unit.
From Wilson and Adams (1992, p. 12).

Students can use the wedge produced by this process to measure angles by seeing how many of them would "fit inside" an angle without gaps or overlaps. For example, the right angle shown in figure 2.7 has a measure of three of these wedges. Wilson and Adams (1992) recommend that students first measure angles by using whole numbers of wedges and then later progress to such fractional parts as halves or fourths.

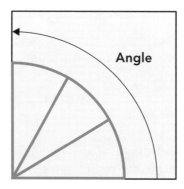

Fig. 2.7. A wedge used to measure angles.
From Wilson and Adams (1992, p. 13).

Of course, a wedge can have many possible sizes. If you allow students to create their own wedges, different students are very likely to have different-sized wedges. This will naturally result in their coming up with different numbers of wedges when measuring the same angle. For example, one student may record a measure of seven of her wedges as the measure of an angle while another student may find that ten of his wedges fill the same angle. These different measurements for the same angle can lead to a productive discussion about the need for standardized units in exactly the same way that measuring other attributes, such as length, with nonstandard units does.

Students may not have had experiences with angles measuring 1 degree, but a right angle is a common point of reference for many people. Examples of right angles abound in everyday experience, including the four corners on the cover of any conventional book. Using these and similar examples can help students who are operating at level 1 of the van Hiele model. While locating examples of right angles is easy, defining a right angle in a way that makes sense to a student in grade 3, 4, or 5 is more challenging. Consider the questions in Reflect 2.2.

Reflect 2.2

The two definitions of *right angle* shown below are similar to those found in textbooks for students in grades 3, 4, and 5:

Definition 1: A *right angle* makes a square corner.

Definition 2: A *right angle* is an angle that measures 90 degrees.

What difficulties might students have in trying to understand these definitions?

What issues might these definitions raise for students as they proceed to higher levels of mathematics?

The word *square* may cause students difficulty in definition 1. First of all, each corner of a square is a right angle, but right angles also appear in other shapes. A right angle may be an angle in a triangle or part of another shape. Definition 1 appears to use the word *square* to mean something other than the two-dimensional shape of the same name. In this case, *square* seems instead to be a synonym for *perpendicular*, as a carpenter might refer to the corner of a room as being *square*.

Definition 2 raises other issues. Although it is true that a right angle measures 90 degrees, the statement that a right angle is an angle that measures 90 degrees will not help a student who does not understand degree measure. Furthermore, angles may be measured in units other than degrees. The unit may be nonstandard, such as a wedge (Wilson and Adams 1992), or it may be standard but not a degree— a radian, perhaps. Therefore, your students' early experiences with angle should not focus on formal definitions, since these are unlikely to help them develop the initial understanding that you intend.

However, you can encourage students to use right angles as reference points for measuring other angles. For example, they can use the corners of sticky notes to identify angles in the classroom that are larger than a right angle ("open more") or that are smaller than a right angle ("open less"). These experiences will prepare students for learning how to measure with a protractor, a skill identified for grade 4 in the Common Core State Standards (CCSSM; NGA Center and CCSSO 2010). According to CCSSM, fourth graders should be able to "measure angles in whole number degrees using a protractor [and] sketch angles of specified measure" (4.MD.6, p. 32). Exploring angles that are "open more" and "open less" than a right angle will also prepare students for classifying angles and naming them conventionally as *obtuse*, *acute*, and so on.

Classifying angles

The Common Core State Standards (NGA Center and CCSSO 2010, p. 32) state that students in grade 4 should be able to "draw and identify lines and angles, and classify shapes by properties of their lines and angles." More specifically, students should have the understanding and skill to do the following:

1. Draw points, lines, line segments, rays, angles (right, acute, obtuse), and perpendicular and parallel lines. Identify these in two-dimensional figures.

2. Classify two-dimensional figures based on the presence or absence of parallel or perpendicular lines, or the presence or absence of angles of a specified size. Recognize right triangles as a category, and identify right triangles. (NGA Center and CCSSO 2010, 4.G.1 and 2, p. 32)

To investigate how students might identify right angles in shapes, we created the Right Angle Shape task, shown in figure 2.8, and gave it to 95 students who were about to complete grade 3, 4, or 5. Examine the task, guided by the questions in Reflect 2.3.

Reflect 2.3

Figure 2.8 shows the Right Angle Shape task, which shows a right trapezoid in four orientations, presented as shapes A–D. Which of these shapes would you expect students in grades 3, 4, and 5 to identify as having right angles? Do you think any of the shapes would give students more trouble than others?

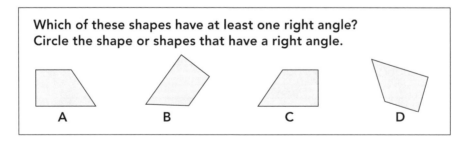

Fig. 2.8. The Right Angle Shape task

Every student in our group identified at least one shape as having a right angle. Figure 2.9 shows the numbers of students in each grade who identified right angles in each of the four shapes.

	Percentage of students identifying right angle(s) in shapes A–D			
Grade / Shape	A	B	C	D
3 (39 students)	36 (92%)	13 (33%)	34 (87%)	27 (69%)
4 (20 students)	18 (90%)	15 (75%)	19 (95%)	18 (90%)
5 (36 students)	36 (100%)	28 (78%)	36 (100%)	35 (97%)
Total (95 students)	90 (95%)	56 (59%)	89 (94%)	80 (84%)

Fig. 2.9. Responses to the Right Angle Shape task

All the shapes in the Right Angle Shape task contain right angles, but students commonly have difficulty recognizing right angles in different orientations (Close 1982, as cited by Mitchelmore [1998]). In fact, the four shapes are congruent; they are reflected or rotated images of the same right trapezoid. Students in grade 4 performed better than those in grade 3. As a group, grade 5 students performed best on this task; all of them noted that shapes A and C contained right angles. Students had the most difficulty identifying the right angles in shape B, which was circled by fewer than half of the students in grade 3. Why did students not identify these right angles? In what different ways did students think about this task? Figures 2.10–2.12 show the work of three different students. Use the questions in Reflect 2.4 to investigate these students' thinking.

Reflect 2.4

Figures 2.10, 2.11, and 2.12, respectively, show the work of Addie (grade 4), Eli (grade 3), and Matthew (grade 3) on the Right Angle Shape task. Examine the responses of these three students. What do these students appear to understand about right angles?

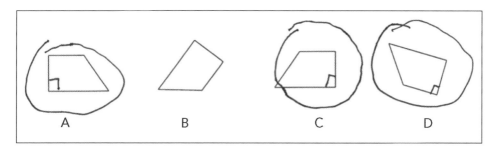

Fig. 2.10. Addie's (grade 4) work on the Right Angle Shape task

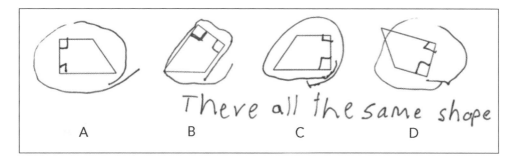

Fig. 2.11. Eli's (grade 3) work on the Right Angle Shape task

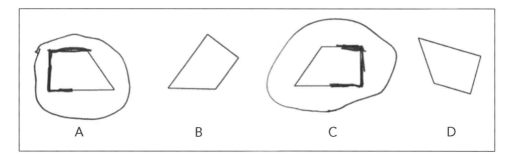

Fig. 2.12. Matthew's (grade 3) work on the Right Angle Shape task

Matthew, whose work is shown in figure 2.12, marked only shapes A and C. He appears to have been operating at level 1 of the van Hiele model. He may have perceived right angles only when the legs of the angles were presented in horizontal or vertical orientations. Overall, 6 of the 95 students (5 in grade 3 and 1 in grade 5) responded in this way. Moreover, our group included 3 students (all in grade 3) who circled only shape A. These students may have had the misconception, described by Mack (2007), that a right angle opens to the right (see fig. 2.13). Additionally, one student in grade 3 and one in grade 4 circled only shape C. Perhaps these students had the misconception that right angles had to be on the right side of the shape.

Helping students understand the multiple meanings of the word *right*, including its use to describe an angle (a right angle), a direction (turn right), or a position (on the right), is important.

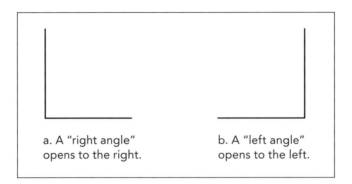

a. A "right angle" opens to the right.

b. A "left angle" opens to the left.

Fig. 2.13. Students' misconceptions of a "right angle" and a "left angle." From Mack (2007, p. 243).

Addie, a fourth grader whose work is shown in figure 2.10, stated that shapes A, C, and D contained right angles, but shape B did not. It is possible that Addie was moving from level 1 to level 2 of the van Hiele model. She recognized that shape D has a right angle but missed the right angles in shape B. Her success with shape D may have been due to the fact that none of the sides of shape D were vertical or horizontal. Addie's response (A, C, and D contained right angles but B did not) was the most common incorrect response within each grade, and it was the most common response given among students in grade 3 (15 out of 39, or 38 percent).

The majority of students in grade 4 (14 of 20, or 70 percent) and grade 5 (28 of 36, or 78 percent), as well as 28 percent of students in grade 3 (11 of 39), responded correctly to the Right Angle Shape task, stating that all four shapes contained at least one right angle. Eli's work, shown in figure 2.11, is one of these responses. In concluding that all the shapes are the same, Eli may have used informal deduction, reasoning that the angles remained the same under rotation and reflection. If he did, he was at level 3 of the van Hiele model.

As stated in the Common Core State Standards, students in grades 3–5 should also be able to identify obtuse angles within shapes. Students should have opportunities to examine examples and non-examples of obtuse angles and consider these in relation to right angles. For example, students could compare the angles in figure 2.14 with the angles in figure 2.15 and then write a description of an obtuse angle. Note that the examples use a variety of orientations.

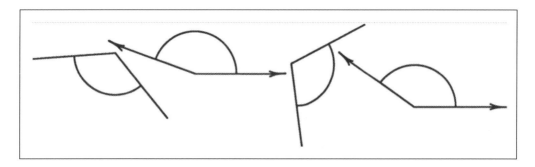

Fig. 2.14. Examples of obtuse angles.
From Page, Wagreich, and Chval (1993a, p. 12).

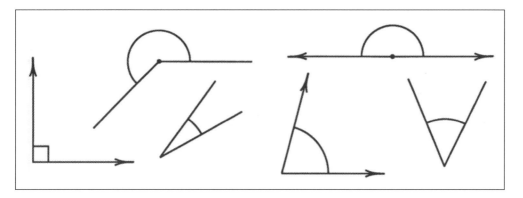

Fig. 2.15. Examples of angles that are not obtuse.
From Page, Wagreich, and Chval (1993a, p. 12).

Some students will describe an obtuse angle as an angle that is larger than a right angle. However, some of the angles in figure 2.15 highlight that this statement is not true, since angles that measure 180 degrees or more are not obtuse angles. Obtuse angles are larger than a right angle but smaller than two right angles (also called a *straight angle*). A similar approach could be used for comparing examples and non-examples of acute angles.

We gave the Obtuse Angle Identification task shown in figure 2.16 to 120 students who were completing grade 3, 4, or 5. Consider the task, guided by the questions in Reflect 2.5.

Reflect 2.5

1. The Obtuse Angle Identification task in figure 2.16 gives students a set of shapes with various sorts of angles. Which shape would you expect students to identify most frequently as containing an obtuse angle? Why do you think so?

2. Which shape containing an obtuse angle would you expect students to miss most frequently? Why do you think so?

3. Which shape not containing an obtuse angle would you expect students to identify most frequently as having an obtuse angle? Why do you think so?

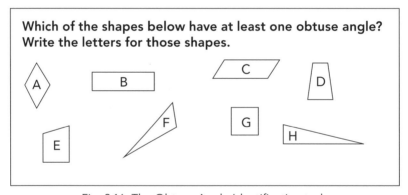

Fig. 2.16. The Obtuse Angle Identification task

Figure 2.17 provides a summary of responses from the students who completed the Obtuse Angle Identification task. Overall, 26 percent of these students correctly identified the shapes A, C, D, E, and F as the only shapes in the set containing obtuse angles. Other students provided partially correct responses by identifying some, but not all, of these five shapes without giving any incorrect responses. The remaining students may have identified some shapes correctly, but they also provided some incorrect responses by selecting a shape that did not contain any obtuse angles.

Grade	Completely correct response of A, C, D, E, and F	Partially correct response with no incorrect responses	Some incorrect responses
3 (36 students)	6 (17%)	22 (61%)	8 (22%)
4 (35 students)	2 (6%)	26 (74%)	7 (20%)
5 (49 students)	23 (47%)	24 (49%)	2 (4%)
Total (120 students)	31 (26%)	72 (60%)	17 (14%)

Fig. 2.17. Summary of 120 responses to the Obtuse Angle Identification task

The data in figure 2.17 show that, in our group, students in grades 3, 4, and 5 were able to identify some shapes with obtuse angles, but most students had difficulty identifying all the shapes with obtuse angles. A small number of students also misidentified shapes B, G, or H as having an obtuse angle. Figure 2.18 shows the numbers and percentages of students who indicated that a specific shape, A–H, in the set shown for the task contained an obtuse angle.

Grade	Correct responses					Incorrect responses		
	A	C	D	E	F	B	G	H
3 (36 students)	19 (53%)	11 (31%)	17 (47%)	18 (50%)	23 (64%)	0	3 (8%)	5 (14%)
4 (35 students)	17 (49%)	20 (57%)	8 (23%)	14 (40%)	24 (69%)	1 (3%)	0	7 (20%)
5 (49 students)	40 (82%)	38 (78%)	31 (63%)	33 (67%)	46 (94%)	0	0	2 (4%)
Total (120 students)	76 (63%)	69 (58%)	56 (47%)	65 (54%)	93 (78%)	1 (1%)	3 (3%)	14 (12%)

Fig. 2.18. Numbers and percentages of students who indicated that a shape shown for the Obtuse Angle Identification task contained an obtuse angle

Within each grade, and overall, the most frequently identified shape that contained an obtuse angle was F, the obtuse triangle. The reason for this may be that students have had experiences with naming triangles on the basis of their angles, an activity that encourages work at level 2 of van Hiele's model. Indeed, this was the case for these particular students in grade 3; however, these same students had not had much practice in analyzing and describing angles in quadrilaterals. Fewer than half of the 120 students circled D, the isosceles trapezoid. A few students at each grade level believed that H, the right triangle, contained an obtuse angle, making it the most frequently misidentified shape.

Students' responses to this task do not reveal which angle (or angles) they identified as obtuse. In using this task in your classroom, you might find it helpful to have students point to, or mark, the obtuse angles on the figure. This strategy will give you greater insight into how your students are identifying (or misidentifying) angles within shapes.

Using different types of questions to address the same content can provide additional insight into students' understanding. With this in mind, we asked students in grades 4 and 5 to draw an obtuse angle. We found that all 56 of these students (20 in grade 4 and 36 in grade 5) were successful on this task, even though some had not provided a correct response on the Obtuse Angle Identification task. To make a further assessment of the students' understanding of vocabulary related to angles, we asked the same students to draw an angle with a measure greater than 90 degrees. Again, all 56 students were successful on this task. This led us to believe that these students understood the meaning of both the word *obtuse* and the phrase "greater than 90 degrees."

These two drawing tasks focused on geometric thinking at level 1 of the van Hiele model. In fact, it is likely that the students drew a picture that matched their mental image of an obtuse angle. To help students describe and reason with angles (level 2 and level 3, respectively), we developed three other drawing tasks, shown in figure 2.19. Let the question in Reflect 2.6 guide your inspection of these tasks.

Reflect 2.6

Examine the drawing tasks shown in figure 2.19. In what different ways would you expect students in grades 3–5 to respond to these tasks?

A. Draw a shape with 4 sides and no right angles.

B. Draw a triangle with 3 acute angles. If this is not possible, explain why.

C. Draw a triangle with 2 obtuse angles. If this is not possible, explain why.

Fig. 2.19. Drawing tasks focusing on van Hiele levels 2 and 3

We gave task A to the same 56 students as before, 20 of whom were completing grade 4 and 36 of whom were completing grade 5. In this task, we were interested in whether our students would be able to think of four-sided shapes beyond squares and rectangles. All but one of the students were successful in this task. They produced a variety of different responses, including trapezoids, nonrectangular parallelograms, and other quadrilaterals with an obtuse angle. A sample of three students' drawings is shown in figure 2.20.

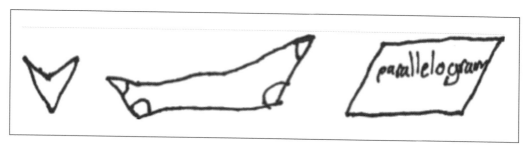

Fig. 2.20. Three students' drawings in response to task A calling for a shape with 4 sides and no right angles

Students will also benefit from analyzing the shapes that they have drawn. To help them focus on the properties of shapes and give you further insight into their thinking, ask such questions as the following:

- "How many obtuse angles does your shape have?"

- "How many acute angles does your shape have?"

- "Does your shape contain any angles that are the same size?"

Creating different shapes that meet the same criteria, and then comparing their work with that of others, can also develop students' thinking. Finally, task A can be modified productively in several ways, as shown in figure 2.21. Examine the modifications to the original task, guided by the questions in Reflect 2.7.

Reflect 2.7

Consider the drawing tasks labeled A1 through A5 in figure 2.21. These tasks modify task A in figure 2.19. Some of these tasks have multiple correct answers, and some are not possible.

1. For the tasks that have multiple correct answers, draw several shapes that meet the criteria.

2. For the tasks that are not possible, explain why they are not possible.

A1.   Draw a shape with 4 sides and only 1 right angle.

A2.   Draw a shape with 4 sides and only 2 right angles.

A3.   Draw a shape with 4 sides and only 3 right angles.

A4.   Draw a shape with 4 sides and no obtuse angles.

A5.   Draw a shape with 4 sides and no acute angles.

Fig. 2.21. Modifications to drawing task A

By giving students opportunities to reason about angles and shapes, teachers can help students make a transition to level 3 of the van Hiele model (see Chapter 3, fig. 3.1, for level 3 descriptors and sample student responses). A student at this level "logically interrelates previously discovered properties/rules by giving or following informal arguments" (Fuys, Geddes, and Tischler 1988, p. 5).

We also gave tasks B and C from figure 2.19 to the 56 students completing grade 4 and grade 5. Almost all the students made a drawing of an acute triangle for drawing task B, as indicated in figure 2.22, which shows a summary of students' work on tasks B and C.

	Response to task B: Draw a triangle with 3 acute angles		Response to task C: Draw a triangle with 2 obtuse angles	
Grade	Correct	Incorrect	Correct	Incorrect
4 (20 students)	18 (90%)	2 (10%)	19 (95%)	1 (5%)
5 (36 students)	31 (86%)	5 (14%)	34 (94%)	2 (6%)
Total (56 students)	49 (88%)	7 (12%)	53 (95%)	3 (5%)

Fig. 2.22. Summary of 56 students' responses to drawing tasks B and C

Some students claimed that it was not possible to draw a triangle with three acute angles. Use the questions in Reflect 2.8 to guide your examination of the response to drawing task B shown in figure 2.23 from a student named Fisher.

Reflect 2.8

Drawing task B in figure 2.19 asks students to draw a triangle with three acute angles or to explain why doing so is not possible. Figure 2.23 shows the response from a fifth grade student, Fisher, to the task. What does Fisher appear to understand about acute angles and triangles?

Fisher gives his reason for thinking the task is not possible. How would you respond to his statement to help him move forward in his mathematical understanding?

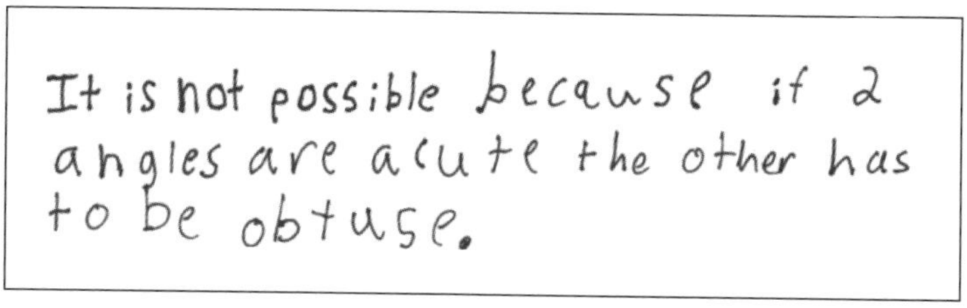

It is not possible because if 2 angles are acute the other has to be obtuse.

Fig. 2.23. Fisher's (grade 5) response to drawing task B

Five of the 56 students, including Fisher, held the same misconception that triangles may have no more than two acute angles. These students were possibly misremembering from the classroom a statement such as, "All triangles have at least two acute angles," simply as, "All triangles have two acute angles." Students who misinterpreted or ignored the qualifying phrase "at least" might hold a misconception that is similar to the misunderstanding reflected in Fisher's statement. One strategy for helping such students would be to ask them to draw a triangle and identify the angles by type (obtuse, right, or acute). You could also provide several different triangles, including right, acute, and obtuse triangles, and ask students to identify the right, acute, and obtuse angles in the figures. By drawing examples and pointing out the types of angles, students at Fisher's level of thinking might develop an understanding of the idea that a triangle can have three acute angles.

Almost all (95 percent) of the students in our group correctly determined that task C, "Draw a triangle with 2 obtuse angles," was impossible. Students gave a variety of explanations of why this was the case. Consider the samples of student work shown in figures 2.24–2.27 while responding to the questions in Reflect 2.9.

Reflect 2.9

Task C in figure 2.19 asks students to draw a triangle with two obtuse angles or explain why this is not possible. Figures 2.24, 2.25, 2.26, and 2.27 show the responses of four fourth- and fifth-grade students—William, AJ, Grace, and Beatrice, respectively—to this task.

Which students provided appropriate reasons?

How might you help such students revise their responses to make them more accurate?

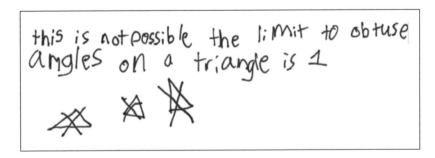

Fig. 2.24. William's (grade 4) response to drawing task C

Because it would form a quadrilateral.

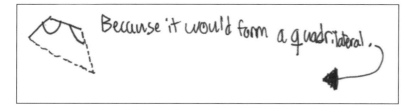

Fig. 2.25. AJ's (grade 4) response to drawing task C

This is not possible because you wouldn't be able to make it a closed shape and it wouldn't be a polygon at all.
no
yes
yes

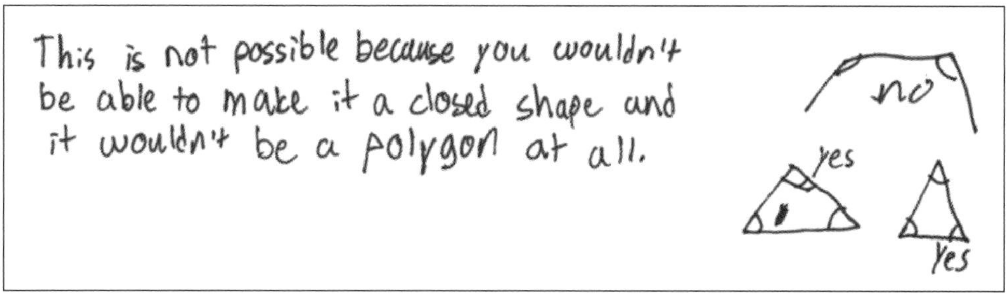

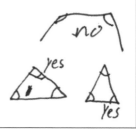

Fig. 2.26. Grace's (grade 5) response to drawing task C

It is not possible because a triangle all angles add up to 180 and if you make a triangle with a obtuse angles it would be more than 180.

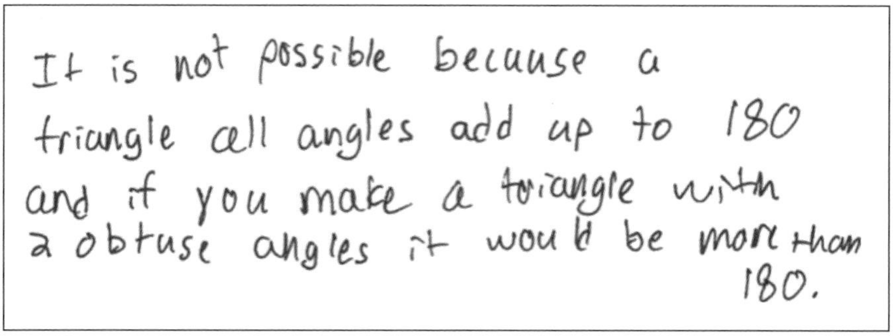

Fig. 2.27. Beatrice's (grade 5) response to drawing task C

William, whose response is shown in figure 2.24, made several attempts to draw a triangle with two obtuse angles, and then crossed out his attempts and wrote, "the limit to obtuse angles on a triangle is 1." This is true, but how William arrived at this fact is unclear. A few attempts may have convinced him that this was the case. Or he may have convinced himself through some sort of informal deduction. Or he may have remembered something that he learned previously. What he wrote does not reveal which of these possibilities, if any, was the case. Twenty other students (5 in grade 4 and 15 in grade 5) responded in a similar manner. Encouraging such students to say more about why a triangle cannot have more than one obtuse angle could elicit useful information about their understanding while at the same time helping them clarify their thinking.

AJ's work appears in figure 2.25. AJ provided a diagram in which he drew one obtuse angle with solid line segments, drew a second obtuse angle with a dashed line, and used another dashed line to close the shape. He then concluded that the figure must be a quadrilateral. AJ was apparently attempting to make a shape with two obtuse angles and in the process realized that the shape could not have three sides. His claim is not completely correct, however, because other shapes besides quadrilaterals have two obtuse angles (see fig. 2.28).

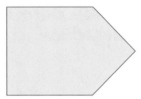

Fig. 2.28. A pentagon with two obtuse angles

Eighteen students (8 in grade 4 and 10 in grade 5) in our group of 56 gave similar responses about the need for a shape with two obtuse angles to have four or more sides. In working with such students, you might ask them to discuss why three sides are not enough in a shape with two obtuse angles.

Grace, whose work appears in figure 2.26, supplied such a reason. She drew two adjacent obtuse angles using three line segments and then claimed that the three sides would not make a closed shape. Eight other students (2 in grade 4 and 6 in grade 5) gave a similar explanation. After several attempts at drawing, one fifth-grade student stated, "The lines would not meet without curving if it has two obtuse angles." These students appear to have used some informal deduction (level 3 of van Hiele's model) in their responses.

Another student, Beatrice, whose work is displayed in figure 2.27, also used informal deduction, but she framed her reasoning in terms of angle measure rather than in relation to construction possibilities in a drawing. She apparently knew that the sum of the interior angles of a triangle is 180 degrees and the sum of the measures of two obtuse triangles would be greater than 180 degrees. Two other students (one in grade 4 and one in grade 5) gave similar responses. Beatrice's response provides proof that the figure is impossible without relying on a set of examples. The variety and range of the students' responses suggest why it is helpful to have students share their reasons with one another. Both AJ and Grace provided specific visual examples of the more abstract statements of William and Beatrice.

Summarizing Pedagogical Content Knowledge for Essential Understanding 2*a*

Teaching the mathematical ideas in this chapter requires specialized knowledge related to the four components presented in the Introduction: learners, curriculum, instructional strategies, and assessment. The four sections that follow summarize some examples of these specialized knowledge bases in relation to Essential Understanding 2*a* in the specific case of angle. Although we separate them to highlight their importance, we also recognize that they are connected and support one another.

Knowledge of learners

Students commonly have some misconceptions about angles. As discussed, students often state that the size of an angle depends on the length of the rays or sides that form it in diagrams (Close 1982; Foxman and Ruddock 1984). Some students have difficulty recognizing specific types of angles in different orientations (Close 1982, as cited by Mitchelmore [1998]). Students may make assumptions about the meaning of *right* in "right angle" and assume that right angles open to the right (Mack 2007). These are important misconceptions to anticipate and challenge as you help your students build essential understandings related to classifying and measuring angles. As demonstrated in figure 2.1, students pay attention to different attributes of angles, including irrelevant attributes such as length of rays and orientation in a diagram. Mathematical tasks should be flexible enough to highlight students' thinking, facilitate productive discussions about these ideas, and move the students to higher levels of thinking.

Knowledge of curriculum

An analysis of your curricular materials can help you determine which problems to use and how to sequence them. As this chapter has shown, varying tasks is important. Using different types of instructional tasks can provide insight into students' understanding. For example, in our group of students in grades 3–5, all students were successful in drawing angles that were described as "obtuse" or "greater than 90 degrees." However, they were not successful with the Obtuse Angle Identification task. Overall, the samples of student work presented in this chapter highlight the challenge of teaching and learning angle concepts. Teaching the concepts related to angles in the Common Core State Standards requires curricular materials that provide numerous experiences with angles—more than just a few pages in a textbook. These tasks should be designed to bring students' misconceptions to the surface so that they can be challenged and should expose students to dynamic, not solely static, representations of angles. Indeed, Wilson and Adams (1992) recommend that students explore both dynamic and static representations of angles throughout the elementary grades, beginning in kindergarten.

How are angles introduced in your curricular materials? Do your materials have a curricular sequence that makes sense and provides sufficient time for students to develop essential understandings related to identifying, measuring, and classifying angles? Do students have opportunities to create their own representations or discuss the meaning of the different components of a representation for angles? Do students have opportunities to explore angles in their environment and by using a variety of tools?

Knowledge of instructional strategies

A multitude of instructional strategies are available for use in teaching students about angles. This section highlights just a few examples. As students begin to work with angles, they need to use physical materials (for example, the hands on a clock face, pipe cleaners, and straws), and they need to draw diagrams. They can use sticky notes in the classroom to identify angles that are larger than a right angle ("more open") or angles that are smaller than a right angle ("less open"), providing them with opportunities to use a right angle as a benchmark to estimate the measures of other angles.

You can also ask students to describe or define angles (Keiser, Klee, and Fitch 2003) to highlight their thinking in relation to attributes and perspectives (for instance, a concept of turning about a point or a relationship between two lines through a point [Mitchelmore 1998]). Students can compare and contrast examples and non-examples of different angle types, as shown in figures 2.14 and 2.15. As students engage in tasks related to angles, discussing different meanings of words such as *right* and *turn* becomes important, as does emphasizing specific mathematical meanings in specialized contexts. Having students sort shapes and categorize them by the number of angles that they contain is also valuable. Moreover, measuring the sizes of those angles by iterating "angle wedges" and also by comparing them to benchmarks such as right angles can develop students' understanding.

Knowledge of assessment

Carefully designed assessment tasks will generate different student strategies, giving teachers information that they can use to help students develop accurate ideas and more sophisticated approaches. For example, giving students a diagram like that in figure 2.2 provides an opportunity for teachers to identify those students who are focusing on the drawn length of the sides of an angle to determine the angle's size. In addition, tasks should give teachers an opportunity to ask extension questions to elicit more information to determine the depth of students' understanding. For example, drawing tasks such as those in figure 2.21 provide opportunities for students to examine angles in quadrilaterals in more depth and permit teachers to follow up with a variety of questions, including, "Why are some of these quadrilaterals impossible to draw?"

Assessment tasks, like instructional tasks, should routinely engage students in creating and interpreting diagrams. Do the tasks used in assessments in your school or district allow you opportunities to understand the ways in which your students are thinking about angles? Do these tasks provide opportunities for students to explain their thinking (consider, for example, the tasks in figure 2.21). Do your tasks use different orientations for angles and shapes? Do they focus on the big ideas related to angles? When do your students interpret diagrams? When do they create their own diagrams? How do their responses to the tasks help you craft your next instructional moves?

Conclusion

The ideas and samples of student work in this chapter have illustrated the complexity and challenges that you face in teaching essential understandings related to angles. If your students are to be successful in developing these understandings, you must not minimize this complexity by trying to integrate all the components of the topic in a few superficial lessons. Helping your students develop an understanding of angles requires giving them opportunities to consider and work with various perspectives and interpretations of angles. This involves using verbal and pictorial representations of angles, as well as offering experiences in identifying and drawing angles and shapes. Although these experiences may help students develop an understanding of angle size, they will nonetheless progress through the van Hiele levels at different rates. You will need to carefully select tasks and pose effective questions to help your students develop these essential understandings—and lay the foundation for classifying shapes by their properties—the topic discussed in Chapter 3.

practice

Chapter 3
Classifying Two-Dimensional Shapes

Essential Understanding 3a
Classification schemes and associated defining properties depend on the purposes and contexts envisioned for mathematical investigation, and multiple classification schemes are often possible.

Essential Understanding 3b
Classification specifies relationships, such as equivalence and inclusion, within and between classes.

Essential Understanding 3c
Classification leads to investigation of criteria for particular classes of shapes, and such investigation can lead in turn to the identification of new properties and relationships among objects in the class.

Classification is "foundational to mathematical activity and discussion," as stated in *Developing Essential Understanding of Geometry and Measurement for Teaching Mathematics in Grades 3–5* (Lehrer and Slovin 2014, p. 10). This assertion readily applies to the context of geometry. Classification involves students in understanding and observing relationships while focusing on properties and attributes that provide a foundation for geometric understanding. When students understand and work with classification, they are moving beyond descriptive and analytic understanding (van Hiele level 2, introduced in Chapter 1) to abstract and relational reasoning (van Hiele level 3). This chapter examines strategies for supporting students' understanding of classification related to two-dimensional shapes.

Fostering Abstract or Relational Thinking: Working toward Essential Understandings 3*a*, 3*b*, and 3*c*

According to Fuys, Geddes, and Tischler (1988), a student with abstract or relational understanding "logically interrelates previously discovered properties/rules by giving or following informal arguments." Figure 3.1 displays excerpts from a table developed by Fuys, Geddes, and Tischler (pp. 64–68) to provide descriptions and sample student responses for geometric thinking at level 3.

Level 3 descriptors *The student—*	Sample student responses

1. a. identifies different sets of properties that characterize a class of figures and tests that these are sufficient;
   b. identifies minimum sets of properties that can characterize a figure;
   c. formulates and uses a definition for a class of figures.
	1. a. Student selects properties that characterize a class of shapes (e.g., squares, parallelograms) and tests by drawings or construction with sticks that these properties are sufficient.
	   b. In describing a square to a friend, student selects from a list of properties the fewest properties that the friend would need to be sure that the shape is a "square."
	   c. Student formulates a definition for a kite and uses it to explain why figures are or are not kites.

2. gives informal arguments (using diagrams, cutout shapes that are folded, or other materials) and—
   a. after drawing a conclusion from given information, justifies it by using logical relationships;
   b. orders classes of shapes;
   c. orders two properties;
   d. discovers new properties by deduction;
   e. interrelates several properties in a family tree.
	2. a. Student concludes that "if angle A = angle B and angle C = angle B, then angle A = angle C because both [angle A and angle C] equal angle B."
	   b. Student responds yes to the question "Is a rectangle a parallelogram?" explaining, "Rectangles have all the properties of parallelograms and also the special property of right angles."
	   c. Student explains, "Opposite sides are equal is not needed because it already says that all four sides are equal," when given a list of properties of a square.
	   d. Student explains that two acute angles in any right triangle add up to 90 degrees because "180 minus the right angle leaves 90 degrees, and that is what is left for the two acute angles."
	   e. Student tells how the area rule for a parallelogram can be derived from the area rule for a rectangle and puts this in a family tree.

3. gives informal deductive arguments and—
   a. follows a deductive argument and can supply parts of the argument;
   b. gives a summary or variation of a deductive argument;
   c. gives deductive arguments on her own.
	3. b. Student who is asked for an explanation of why "opposite angles of a parallelogram are congruent" is not able to give one on his own but can follow an explanation given for one pair of opposite angles and then can summarize it in his own words and also explain why the other pair of opposite angles is equal.
	   c. Student gives an explanation on her own for "opposite angles of a parallelogram are equal."

Fig. 3.1. Descriptors for van Hiele level 3 (Abstract/Relational) and sample student responses. Adapted from Fuys, Geddes, and Tischler (1988, pp. 64–68).

Level 3 descriptors The student—	Sample student responses
4. gives more than one explanation to prove something and justifies these explanations by using family trees.	4. Student gives two different explanations for why a parallelogram with a right angle is a rectangle.
5. informally recognizes difference between a statement and its converse.	5. In a discussion of lines cut by a transversal, student discovers, "Oh, if you make the angles equal, then the lines are parallel" and "Oh, if you make the lines parallel, then the angles are equal." When asked if these statements are the same, the student realizes, "No, in one case you start by making the lines parallel lines, and that makes the angles equal; and in the other case you do the opposite—you start by making the angles equal, and that makes the lines parallel."
6. recognizes the role of deductive argument and approaches problems in a deductive manner but— a. does *not* grasp the meaning of deduction in an axiomatic sense (e.g., does *not* see the need for definitions and basic assumptions); b. does *not* formally distinguish between a statement and its converse; c. does *not* yet establish interrelationships among networks of theorems.	6. Student recognizes the role of logical explanations or deductive arguments in establishing facts (versus an inductive, empirical approach) and says (after giving a logical explanation), "I know that the angle sum for every pentagon is 540 degrees, and I don't have to measure." However, student has yet to experience "proof" in an axiomatic sense (i.e., using postulates, axioms, and definitions).

Fig 3.1. *Continued*

Beginning to build the foundations for thinking at this level in the elementary grades is important. Many students do not lay the groundwork for level 3 thinking this early, and as a result, as Clements and Battista (1992) report,

> Almost 40% [of students] finish high school geometry below Level 2 (Burger & Shaughnessy, 1986; Suydam, 1985; Usiskin, 1982). In fact, because many students have not developed Level 3 thought processes, they may not benefit from additional work in formal geometry because their knowledge and the information presented will be organized differently. (p. 430)

Furthermore, some students may reason at different levels for different shapes. For example, a student may reason informally about the properties of triangles but focus on specific attributes of quadrilaterals. Burger and Shaughnessy (1986) note, "Mayberry (1983) also found that students can be on different levels for different concepts and that many students never reach the level of formal deduction, a conclusion shared by Usiskin (1982)" (pp. 41–42).

Using definitions to classify shapes

In Chapter 1, we discussed students' work in identifying rectangles and describing their attributes and properties. To gain further insight into their understanding of rectangles, we also asked students to complete the Rectangle Definition task, shown in figure 3.2. Consider this task as you respond to the questions in Reflect 3.1.

What is the definition of a rectangle?

Fig. 3.2. The Rectangle Definition task

Reflect 3.1

Figure 3.2 shows the Rectangle Definition task. What definitions would you expect from students in grades 3, 4, and 5?

How would you expect responses from students in grades 3–5 to differ by grade level?

We gave this task to 46 third-grade students, 38 fourth-grade students, and 48 fifth-grade students. Figure 3.3 reports the ideas included in students' definitions by grade level.

Emphasis	Number of responses, grade 3 (46 students)	Number of responses, grade 4 (38 students)	Number of responses, grade 5 (48 students)
A shape with 4 sides	7 (15%)	7 (18%)	19 (40%)
2 pairs of equal sides	1 (2%)	1 (3%)	10 (21%)
2 short sides and 2 long sides	9 (20%)	4 (11%)	8 (17%)
Parallelogram	0	3 (8%)	3 (6%)
Quadrilateral	7 (15%)	5 (13%)	17 (35%)
2 pairs of parallel sides	1 (2%)	15 (39%)	18 (38%)
4 right angles/vertices/corners	2 (4%)	6 (16%)	16 (33%)

Fig. 3.3. A summary of the emphases of students' definitions of *rectangle*

Emphasis	Number of responses, grade 3 (46 students)	Number of responses, grade 4 (38 students)	Number of responses, grade 5 (48 students)
2 squares/stretched square	10 (22%)	2 (5%)	2 (4%)
No answer	9 (20%)	8 (21%)	0

Note: Percentages total to more than 100% by grade level because the tallies of responses include multiple aspects of a student's response.

Fig. 3.3. *Continued*

Ten third-grade students referred to squares in their definitions. The following are several examples:

- "It is an object with 2 squares mashed together to make 1 shape called a rectangle."

- "4 sides, is a stretched square."

- "A rectangle is a shape like a square but longer."

- "I think of it as a longer square."

- "A square stretched out I think."

One student, Alex, drew a picture to help convey the meaning of his words. His work is shown in figure 3.4.

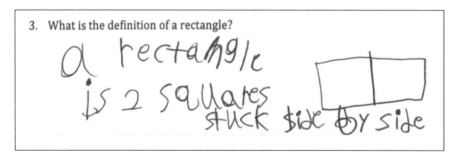

Fig. 3.4. Alex's (grade 3) definition of a rectangle

Responses provided by two fourth-grade students and two fifth-grade students also refer to squares in ways that suggest that a square is not a rectangle, demonstrating that this misconception may persist for several years. Furthermore, Burger and

Shaughnessy (1986) suggest that confusion about the relationship between squares and rectangles may continue into the middle grades. They present the case of Amy, an eighth grader, as evidence:

> In describing the shapes, she [Amy] explicitly excluded squares from rectangles, saying that rectangles have "two sides equal and parallel to each other. Two longer sides are equal and parallel to each other, and they connect at 90 degrees." (p. 39)

The goal in grades 3–5 is for students to develop a dynamic view of a rectangle, recognizing that rotating or sliding a rectangle does not change whether the shape is a rectangle, while also recognizing that morphing a shape—stretching and distorting it—will not always result in a shape with the same classification. Renne (2004) reported similar results to those previously discussed from fourth-grade students as they debated similarities and differences between squares and rectangles.

To appreciate the challenge and importance of writing and working with mathematical definitions, consider some examples of definitions by students in grades 3–5. Figure 3.5 presents seven definitions offered by students for a rectangle. After examining the definitions, respond to the questions in Reflect 3.2.

a. A rectangle is a quadrilateral.

b. A rectangle is a quadrilateral with 4 right angles.

c. A rectangle is a polygon with 2 sets of parallel lines.

d. A rectangle has two pairs of parallel sides and one pair of parallel sides is longer than the other pair.

e. A rectangle is a four-sided polygon. It is a closed shape, with straight line segments.

f. A rectangle is a polygon with 4 right angles.

g. A rectangle is a parallelogram with 4 sides.

Fig. 3.5. "Definitions" of a rectangle generated by students in grades 3–5

Reflect 3.2

Examine the students' definitions for a rectangle, shown in figure 3.5. Which are true statements about rectangles?

Which definitions are *sufficient* (that is, provide enough information) to define a rectangle?

For each definition that is not sufficient, draw a picture of a shape that meets the definition's requirements but is not a rectangle.

Not surprisingly, many students struggled with the task of writing a correct mathematical definition for a rectangle. All the statements shown in figure 3.5 are true except for (d), which is not true for squares and so is not true for rectangles. Although the remaining six statements are true, five of them—all but (b)—are insufficient as definitions of a rectangle. For example, (a), "A rectangle is a quadrilateral," is true, but other nonrectangular shapes are also quadrilaterals—a trapezoid, for example. Two of the five insufficient definitions—(e) and (g)—include information that is superfluous or redundant in addition to omitting information that is necessary. For example, (g) states that a rectangle is a parallelogram with four sides, but all parallelograms have four sides, so including both conditions is unnecessary.

As these difficulties in writing sufficient definitions of *rectangle* demonstrate, few students in grades 3–5 are likely to be functioning at van Hiele level 3 with respect to rectangles. Reflect 3.3 invites you to reconsider the insufficient definitions in figure 3.5 in relation to the four non-rectangles shown in figure 3.6.

Reflect 3.3

Examine the nonrectangular shapes in figure 3.6. Do any of these shapes fit "definitions" offered by students, as shown in figure 3.5?

Which shapes fit which definitions?

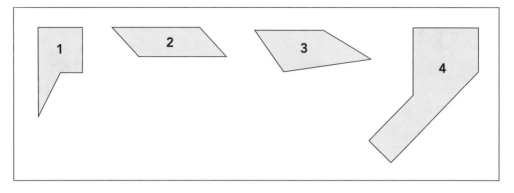

Fig. 3.6. Non-rectangles that may fit insufficient "definitions" offered by students

How often do you provide opportunities for your students to generate, analyze, and compare definitions? Do you help your students develop their understanding of the nature and purpose of definitions, especially in mathematics? Citing Edwards and Ward (2004), Usiskin and Griffin (2008) argue that such work is important to counteract misconceptions that students have about definitions:

> Yet many teachers and students do not realize there is a choice of definitions for mathematical terms. And even those who realize there is a choice may not know who decides which definition of any mathematical term is better, and under what criteria. Finally, rarely are the mathematical implications of various choices discussed. As a result, many students misuse and otherwise do not understand the role of definition in mathematics (Edwards and Ward 2004). (pp. ix–x)

Usiskin and Griffin analyzed definitions of quadrilaterals used in high school geometry textbooks. They reported the definitions for rectangles that were used most frequently, as shown in figure 3.7. Consider these definitions, guided by the questions in Reflect 3.4.

Reflect 3.4

How do the definitions of *rectangle* shown in figure 3.7 from high school textbooks compare with the student-generated definitions in figure 3.5?

How do these textbook definitions compare with the definitions in the curricular materials that you use in grades 3–5?

A rectangle is...	Number of geometry textbooks
a parallelogram with four right angles.	35
a parallelogram in which at least one angle is a right angle.	30
an equiangular parallelogram.	7
a quadrilateral that has four right angles.	6

Fig. 3.7. Definitions for rectangles used in high school geometry textbooks

According to Usiskin and Griffin (2008), definitions given in curricular materials for the elementary grades are more likely to be everyday definitions than to be mathematical definitions:

> Mathematics textbooks at the elementary school level often follow the standard dictionary conception of definition. From a mathematical perspective, the meanings of terms are often more accurately characterized as *descriptions* rather than as definitions. At the high school level, and particularly in geometry textbooks, authors tend to provide mathematically precise definitions of terms…. However, many textbook definitions do not adhere to an additional criterion that is generally standard among mathematicians, that a definition not contain superfluous conditions. For instance, the most common definition of rectangle in U.S. geometry textbooks is "a parallelogram with four right angles." Yet a parallelogram with just one right angle can be shown to be a rectangle, making the criterion of the other three right angles superfluous to the definition. (p. 7)

Not surprisingly, in our group of students in grades 3–5, many students wrote the same definitions for a rectangle in response to the Rectangle Definition task (see fig. 3.2) as for the task that required them to write down everything that they knew to be true about all rectangles (see Chapter 1, fig. 1.9). Mack, a fourth-grade student, questioned why we would pose both tasks, as shown in figure 3.8.

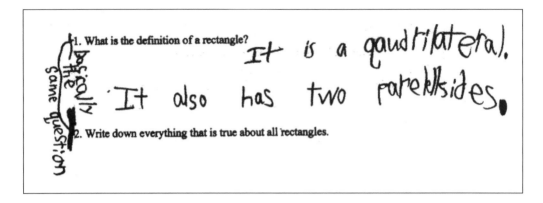

Fig. 3.8. Mack's (grade 4) response to two tasks related to rectangles

In many cases, however, posing both questions provided additional information about what students understood or misunderstood. For example, Jennie, a third-grade student wrote, "A rectangle is 4 sided shape" as her definition. However, for the task related to what she knew about rectangles, she wrote, "A rectangle has 4 sides and if you divide is two squares." The second task revealed her van Hiele level 1 image of a rectangle as two squares, which ten of her third-grade peers also suggested in their definitions.

Posing both tasks also provides an opportunity to discuss the difference between definitions and attributes of rectangles. Usiskin and Griffin (2008) state that a definition of a mathematical object typically classifies the object "first by identifying the category to which an object belongs, and then by indicating how this object is distinguished from other objects in that category" (p. 3). For example, Michael, a third-grade student, gave as his definition of a rectangle, "A quadrilateral with 4 right angles." First, his definition classifies rectangles within the category of quadrilaterals, and then it distinguishes rectangles from other quadrilaterals with the condition of having 4 right angles. Attributes and properties, in contrast, are characteristics that belong to the object on the basis of the definition. In the task that asked students to write everything that is true for all rectangles, Michael included the following attributes, which result from his definition:

- Rectangles have 4 sides, vertices, and right angles.

- Rectangles are squares and are not.

- Rectangles are parallelograms.

- Rectangles are polygons.

- Rectangles are closed.

- Rectangles are quadrilaterals.

Deepening understanding of the definition of a shape is a step that can help students begin to develop their understanding of relationships among various shapes, while recognizing that some shapes are special cases of other shapes. Gutiérrez and Jaime (1998) explain that "students in level 1 can only understand only exclusive classifications, since they do not accept nor recognize any kind of logical relationship between classes" (p. 30), whereas "students in level 3 [have] the ability to make inclusive classifications of families. Thus, those students who say, for instance, that squares are not rectangles, are assigned to level 2" (pp. 30–31). This is to say that students at level 1 would not recognize that squares could also be characterized as rectangles, quadrilaterals, or parallelograms. The next section explores ways to deepen students' understanding of these relationships.

Offering informal arguments to relate shapes

The Common Core State Standards (National Governors Association Center for Best Practices and Council of Chief State School Officers [NGA Center and CCSSO] 2010) emphasize the importance of having students in grades 3–5 identify the attributes of shapes in different categories and use shared attributes to create and define new categories. Figure 3.9 shows the relevant standards for grades 3 and 5. As students mature in their understanding, they should be given opportunities to demonstrate an understanding of classification and hierarchies. Figures 3.10 and 3.11 show two examples of hierarchical classifications from Usiskin and Griffin (2008).

Common Core State Standards for Mathematics, Grades 3 and 5

Geometry, grade 3

Reason with shapes and their attributes.

1. Understand that shapes in different categories (e.g., rhombuses, rectangles, and others) may share attributes (e.g., having four sides), and that the shared attributes can define a larger category (e.g., quadrilaterals). Recognize rhombuses, rectangles, and squares as examples of quadrilaterals, and draw examples of quadrilaterals that do not belong to any of these subcategories.

Fig. 3.9. Classification of 2-D shapes in grades 3 and 5.
CCSSM 3.G.1 and 5.G.3 and 4 (NGA Center and CCSSO 2010, pp. 26 and 38).

Common Core State Standards for Mathematics, Grades 3 and 5

Geometry, grade 5

Classify two-dimensional figures into categories based on their properties.

3. Understand that attributes belonging to a category of two-dimensional figures also belong to all subcategories of that category. *For example, all rectangles have four right angles and squares are rectangles, so all squares have four right angles.*

4. Classify two-dimensional figures in a hierarchy based on properties.

Fig. 3.9. *Continued*

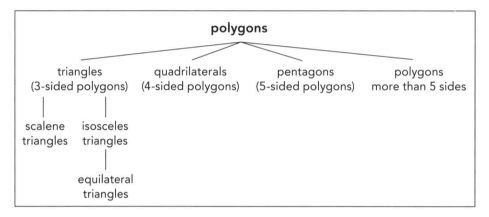

Fig. 3.10. A hierarchical classification of polygons, based on their properties. From Usiskin and Griffin (2008, p. 7).

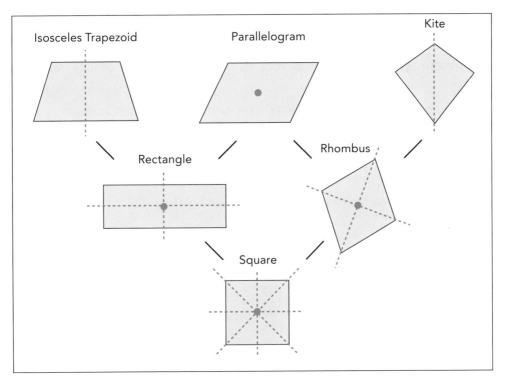

Fig. 3.11. A hierarchical classification of quadrilaterals, based on symmetries.
From Usiskin and Griffin (2008, p. 75).

To assess students' understanding and use of definitions and classification at the fourth- and fifth-grade levels, we posed the task shown in figure 3.12. This task modifies an item from the National Assessment of Educational Progress (Strutchens and Blume 1997) by adding some student responses and slightly altering the original task. Examine our modified task, using the questions in Reflect 3.5 to focus your analysis.

Reflect 3.5

The task in figure 3.12 asks students to evaluate three fictitious students' efforts to draw a square, given the two points shown. How would you anticipate that your own students would respond to these students' efforts?

What incorrect efforts would you would expect your students to accept as correct?

Reflect 3.5, *continued*

What misconceptions might lead your students to select those incorrect efforts?

What would you do to help students who have those misconceptions overcome them and move forward?

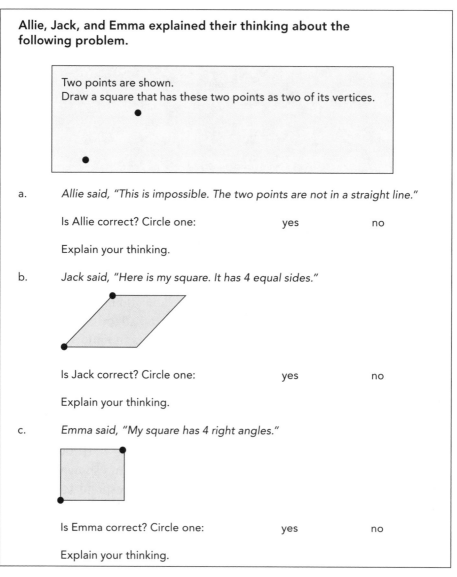

Allie, Jack, and Emma explained their thinking about the following problem.

> Two points are shown.
> Draw a square that has these two points as two of its vertices.

a.   *Allie said, "This is impossible. The two points are not in a straight line."*

   Is Allie correct? Circle one: yes   no

   Explain your thinking.

b.   *Jack said, "Here is my square. It has 4 equal sides."*

   Is Jack correct? Circle one: yes   no

   Explain your thinking.

c.   *Emma said, "My square has 4 right angles."*

   Is Emma correct? Circle one: yes   no

   Explain your thinking.

Fig. 3.12. Fictitious students' responses to a task to draw a square with two given vertices. Adapted from Strutchens and Blume (1997, p. 169).

The 86 fourth and fifth graders in our group answered these three yes-no questions in seven different ways. The three most popular responses are displayed in figure 3.13. The shaded row highlights the correct answer, which is that none of the three students are correct.

Response	Fourth-grade responses (37 students)	Fifth-grade responses (49 students)
None of the three students are correct.	7 (19%)	24 (49%)
Only Emma is correct.	11 (30%)	14 (29%)
Both Jack and Emma are correct.	13 (35%)	1 (2%)

Fig. 3.13. Common responses to the task in figure 3.12

Although the fifth-grade students were more successful with this task than their fourth-grade peers, the majority were incorrect. Different students emphasized a variety of attributes in their reasoning. For example, fourth and fifth graders emphasized the following reasons why Jack's shape is not a square:

a. The angles are not the same.

b. The sides are not the same length.

c. The shape does not have 4 right angles.

d. The shape does not have 4 straight sides.

e. The shape does not have a line of symmetry.

Many students referred to an idea that they held that squares are "straight" and rhombuses are "slanted." In fact, responses like (d) highlight some misconceptions that students have about "straight" or their difficulty in using proper vocabulary to describe the angles. Some students in our group attended to some attributes of squares but not others. Figures 3.14–3.16 present work from three fifth-grade students. Examine the work, guided by the questions in Reflect 3.6.

Reflect 3.6

Figures 3.14, 3.15, and 3.16 show the responses of three fifth graders, Luz, Didem, and David, respectively, to the work of two fictitious students, Jack and Emma, shown in figure 3.12.

Which attributes of a square did the students use to defend their interpretations of the fictitious students' answers?

How would you characterize the mathematical understandings and misunderstandings that these students exhibited?

If your students gave these responses, what specific strategies or questions would you use to move them forward?

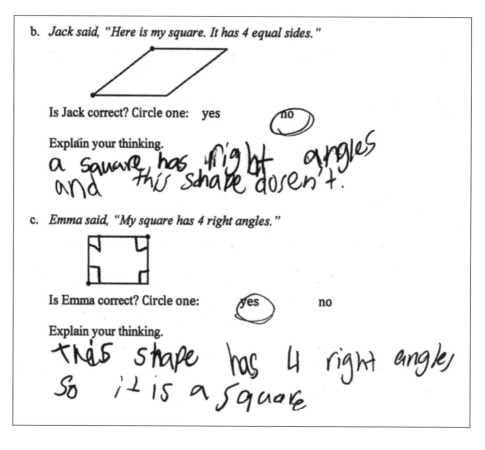

Fig. 3.14. Luz's (grade 5) response to the work of two fictitious students, Jack and Emma

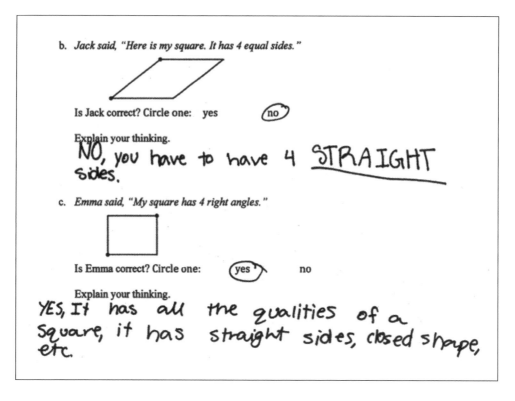

Fig. 3.15. Didem's (grade 5) response to the work of two fictitious students, Jack and Emma

Consider Luz's responses, shown in figure 3.14. Luz examined the shapes drawn by Jack and Emma on the basis of a single attribute—right angles. Her exclusive use of this attribute resulted in a correct appraisal of Jack's work (b) but an incorrect assessment of Emma's work (c).

By contrast, Didem's responses, shown in figure 3.15, focused on the sides of a square, which she claimed must be "straight." It appears that Didem viewed horizontal and vertical lines as straight, but other lines did not qualify.

David provided a surprising response. His work, shown in figure 3.16, takes account of several attributes of squares, including equal sides, vertices, and parallelism, yet he doesn't attend to the necessity of right angles. Consider David's response as you respond to the questions in Reflect 3.7.

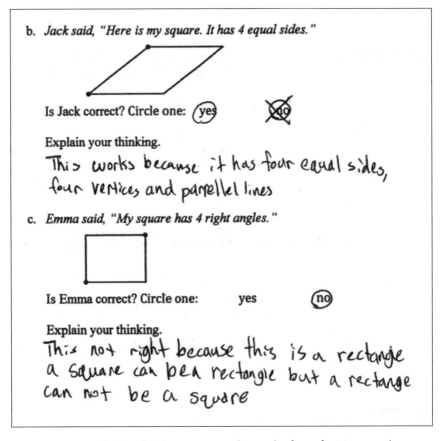

b. *Jack said, "Here is my square. It has 4 equal sides."*

Is Jack correct? Circle one: (yes)   ~~no~~

Explain your thinking.

This works because it has four equal sides, four vertices and parrellel lines

c. *Emma said, "My square has 4 right angles."*

Is Emma correct? Circle one: yes   (no)

Explain your thinking.

This not right because this is a rectangle a square can be a rectangle but a rectangle can not be a square

Fig. 3.16. David's (grade 5) response to the work of two fictitious students, Jack and Emma

Reflect 3.7

Examine David's reasoning about Emma's answer, shown in figure 3.16. What do you think David was trying to convey? What is problematic about his statement?

David demonstrated some knowledge of the relationship between squares and rectangles. Specifically, he showed his awareness of the existence of a hierarchy in which all squares are rectangles. Mathematics textbooks for students in grades 3–5 typically define both a rectangle and a square in terms of their properties, and then state, "A square is a special kind of rectangle," or, "A square is also a rectangle." Unfortunately, stating this fact does not immediately foster an understanding of the relationship between squares and rectangles—that all squares are included in the category of rectangles, and that everything that is true for rectangles is also true for squares.

Van de Walle, Karp, and Bay-Williams (2010) describe the geometric reasoning of students at van Hiele level 3 (Abstract/Relational) as follows:

> As students begin to be able to think about properties of geometric objects without constraints of a particular object, they are able to develop relationships between and among these properties. "If all four angles are right angles, the shape must be a rectangle. If it is a square, all angles are right angles. If it is a square, it must be a rectangle." ... Observations go beyond properties themselves and begin to focus on arguments *about* the properties. Students at [this level] will be able to follow and appreciate an informal deductive argument about shapes and their properties. "Proofs" may be more intuitive than rigorously deductive; however, there is an appreciation that a logical argument is compelling. (p. 403)

To investigate students' understanding and use of informal arguments about relationships among shapes further, we posed the task in figure 3.17 to students in fourth and fifth grades. Examine the task, using the questions in Reflect 3.8 to focus your thinking.

Reflect 3.8

Figure 3.17 shows a task designed to explore students' understanding of squares as rectangles. Examine the task, and then answer the following questions:

What mathematical ideas might this task bring out?

How would you expect your students to respond to the thinking of the two fictitious students, Mary and Jeremiah?

Mary and Jeremiah were talking about this shape:

a. Mary says that the shape is a rectangle because the shape has 4 right angles and the opposite sides are the same length. Since this shape has these, it must be a rectangle.

Do you agree with Mary?   Circle one: yes   no
Explain your thinking.

b. Jeremiah says that it is not a rectangle because rectangles have two long sides and two short sides.

Do you agree with Jeremiah?   Circle one: yes   no
Explain your thinking.

Fig. 3.17. A task to explore the inclusion of squares in the category of rectangles

In designing this task, we intentionally made the shape a square but did not call it a square. Two fictitious students, Mary and Jeremiah, are discussing the shape. Mary's thinking about the shape relies on definitions and classification and leads her to identify the shape correctly; Jeremiah's thinking exhibits a common misconception that keeps him from the correct identification.

We gave this task to 20 fourth-grade students and 36 fifth-grade students; figure 3.18 summarizes their responses. Overall, slightly more than half (30 out of 56) of these students gave the correct response—that is, they agreed with Mary and disagreed with Jeremiah (see the highlighted row in fig. 3.18). We were interested to see that the fourth graders tended to be more successful on the task than the fifth graders, 44 percent of whom disagreed with Mary and agreed with Jeremiah (see row 2 in the table in fig. 3.18).

Response	Fourth-grade responses (20 students)	Fifth-grade responses (36 students)
Agreed with Mary, disagreed with Jeremiah	12 (60%)	18 (50%)
Disagreed with Mary, agreed with Jeremiah	6 (30%)	16 (44%)
Agreed with both Mary and Jeremiah	2 (10%)	1 (3%)
Disagreed with both Mary and Jeremiah	0	1 (3%)

Fig. 3.18. Summary of fourth and fifth graders' responses to the task in figure 3.17

Examining the students' explanations of their responses to the task gives further insight into their thinking. Reflect 3.9 poses questions about the response of Sheriff, a fifth-grade student, presented in figure 3.19, to Mary's statement in figure 3.17. Examine Sheriff's response, guided by the questions posed.

Reflect 3.9

Figure 3.19 shows the explanation offered by Sheriff, a fifth grader who agreed with Mary that the shape in the task shown in figure 3.17 is a rectangle. What does Sheriff appear to have understood about classification of squares and rectangles?

What, if anything, is problematic about his statement?

Fig. 3.19. Sheriff's (grade 5) response to Mary's statement in figure 3.17

Sheriff gave a correct response to the multiple-choice yes-no question. His supporting explanation was representative of the most common reasoning in our group of fourth and fifth graders. Similar statements were given by 14 of 56, or 25 percent, of students. However, the statement, "A square can be a rectangle, but a rectangle can't be a square," is not correct. According to the commonly accepted classification of quadrilaterals, a square *is* a rectangle. Stating that a square "can be" a rectangle leaves open the possibility that some squares may not be rectangles. This is analogous to stating that people *can be* mammals rather than that all people *are* mammals. On the other hand, a rectangle *can be* a square. Some rectangles are not squares, but rectangles with four sides of equal length are squares. In fact, an infinite number of different rectangles can be drawn that are also squares, as can an infinite number of different rectangles that are not squares.

A few students gave responses that sounded similar to Sheriff's written explanation but had a different meaning. Akira (grade 5) claimed, "A square can also be classified as a rectangle." Joanne (grade 4) stated, "Rectangles can also be square." Both Akira and Joanne are correct, and they use language appropriately to convey their understanding of the classification of quadrilaterals and the inclusion of squares within the category of rectangles. Because of the difficulty that some students in grades 3–5 have with language, providing many opportunities for them to write and talk about classification and hierarchies is valuable. These experiences should be in a variety of settings. They should involve 3-D solids as well as 2-D shapes and should also extend beyond mathematics, to include examples from science, social studies, or language arts.

Page, Wagreich, and Chval (1995) provide an activity that may help students in grades 3–5 develop an understanding of definitions and classification. One set of shapes contains examples of a particular shape while another set contains non-examples. Figure 3.20 displays an example of such an activity for rectangles.

Another activity, suggested by Van de Walle, Karp, and Bay-Williams (2010), challenges students to identify and name the "mystery property" of a set of shapes, as illustrated in figure 3.21. In this activity, students are shown three sets of shapes. The shapes in the first set all share a particular property, which none of the shapes in the second set have. Students must determine which shapes in the third set have this property. To complete the activity, students must not only identify shapes but also communicate in words to name the property in question. In the case in figure 3.21, the mystery property is "obtuse triangle."

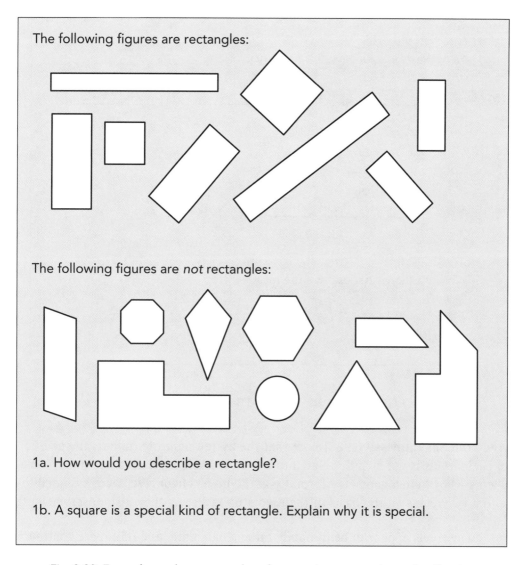

The following figures are rectangles:

The following figures are *not* rectangles:

1a. How would you describe a rectangle?

1b. A square is a special kind of rectangle. Explain why it is special.

Fig. 3.20. Examples and non-examples of rectangles, suggesting a classification.
From Page, Wagreich, and Chval (1995, p. 13).

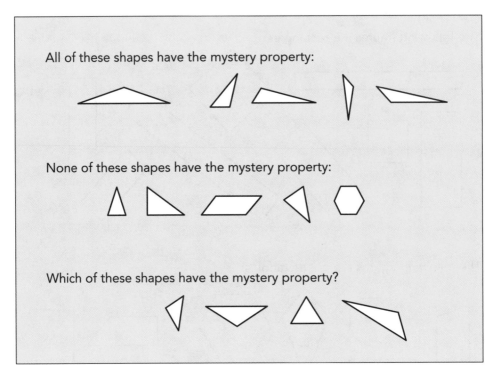

All of these shapes have the mystery property:

None of these shapes have the mystery property:

Which of these shapes have the mystery property?

Fig. 3.21. Mystery property task.
Based on Van de Walle, Karp, and Bay-Williams (2010, p. 413).

Burger and Shaughnessy (1986) note that the assignment of students to specific van Hiele levels is not strictly related to age or to grade level. In their study, some students who studied geometry formally at the high school level were assigned to the first two levels on the basis of their work on tasks. As they also observe,

> The levels appear to be dynamic rather than static and of a more continuous nature than their discrete descriptions would lead one to believe. Students may move back and forth between levels quite a few times while they are in transition from one level to the next. Our data particularly support this phenomenon between Levels 1 and 2. (p. 45)

Understanding these ideas is critical to recognizing that a particular student may not fall neatly into one level. Gutiérrez and Jaime (1998) identify different processes of reasoning and summarize the main characteristics of each process used to distinguish among students at different levels. Their table, reproduced in figure 3.22, provides a framework to assist teachers as they select instructional tasks and assess students' reasoning. Moreover, it can serve as a guide for future activities that students should experience as they progress to more advanced levels.

	Level 1	Level 2	Level 3	Level 4
Recognition	Physical attributes	Mathematical properties	——	——
Use of definitions	——	Only definitions with simple structure	Any definition	Accept several equivalent definitions
Formulation of definitions	List of physical properties	List of mathematical properties	Set of necessary and sufficient properties	Can prove the equivalence of definitions
Classification	Exclusive, based on physical attributes	Exclusive, based on mathematical attributes	Can move among inclusive and exclusive	——
Proof	——	Verification with examples	Informal logical proofs	Formal mathematical proofs

Fig. 3.22. Distinctive attributes of the processes of reasoning in each van Hiele level. From Gutiérrez and Jaime (1998, p. 32).

Summarizing Pedagogical Content Knowledge to Support Essential Understandings 3a, 3b, and 3c

Teaching the mathematical ideas in this chapter requires specialized knowledge related to the four components presented in the Introduction: learners, curriculum, instructional strategies, and assessment. The four sections that follow summarize some examples of these specialized knowledge bases in relation to Essential Understandings 3a, 3b, and 3c. Although we separate them to highlight their importance, we also recognize that they are connected and support one another.

Knowledge of learners

The van Hiele (1958) framework can help you understand your students' cognitive development in relation to geometric shapes. In addition, figure 3.1, adapted from Fuys, Geddes, and Tischler (1988), provides useful examples of possible student responses at level 3 of the van Hiele framework. Not only can these examples help you to anticipate student responses in relation to the van Hiele levels of geometric development but they can also guide you as you select and design tasks and discussion questions. As your students mature in their understanding, you should offer them opportunities to demonstrate an understanding of classification and hierarchies.

As stated in the Common Core State Standards for third grade, students should "understand that shapes in different categories (e.g., rhombuses, rectangles, and others) may share attributes (e.g., having four sides), and that the shared attributes can define a larger category (e.g., quadrilaterals)" (NGA Center and CCSSO 2010, p. 26). Different students will focus on and emphasize different attributes in their reasoning, as illustrated by the thinking that our students demonstrated in response to the task in figure 3.12. Luz, a fifth grader (see fig. 3.14), examined the shapes created by the fictitious students Jack and Emma on the basis of a single attribute—right angles. Another fifth grader, Didem (see fig. 3.15), focused on what she viewed as "straight sides." A third fifth grader, David (see fig. 3.16), included several attributes (equal sides, vertices, and parallelism), yet he did not attend to the necessity of the right angles. As you work with your students' reasoning about ways of classifying 2-D shapes, you will discover that determining which attributes students identify for specific shapes is important, but so is determining whether they recognize that shared attributes may define a larger category.

Knowledge of curriculum

Current textbooks approach definitions for rectangles in a variety of ways, as shown by Usiskin and Griffin (2008). Which definitions do your curricular materials introduce for 2-D shapes? Do they introduce students to important ideas, such as the difference between descriptions and definitions and the meaning of classification and hierarchies? Do your curricular tasks require students to articulate their reasoning or examine the reasoning of others? Do they form a curricular sequence that makes sense and provides sufficient time for students to develop these ideas? Carefully examining definitions presented in your curricular materials is important, as is recognizing that you may need to replace these definitions with accurate ones that are appropriate for the grade level or levels that you teach.

You may also need to supplement your curricular materials with additional, different images of 2-D shapes so that your students do not form inappropriate concept images (Tall and Vinner 1981). For example, if students see only "typical" rectangles that appear to be approximately the size of two adjacent, congruent squares, their thinking is likely to be similar to that of third-grade student Alex (see fig. 3.4).

Knowledge of instructional strategies

Teachers can draw on many and varied instructional strategies in helping their students reason about classification and classify 2-D shapes. This section highlights two examples.

- *Drawing counterexamples that "fit" students' descriptions to challenge their thinking.* As this chapter has demonstrated, students often create inaccurate or insufficient descriptions or definitions of two-dimensional shapes (see fig. 3.5). Drawing counterexamples that "fit" their descriptions can help them confront and correct the shortcomings in their thinking. For example, if a student states, "A rectangle is a quadrilateral," you can draw a quadrilateral that is not a rectangle (two examples appear in fig. 3.6) and say, "Oh, so this shape is a rectangle?" You could also ask the student (or the class) to draw as many different types of quadrilaterals as possible and then ask, "Are all of these quadrilaterals also rectangles?"

- *Providing opportunities for students to generate, analyze, and compare definitions for specific 2-D shapes.* You must also help students understand and distinguish among definitions, descriptions, and lists of attributes. Furthermore, you must help them examine and discuss ideas related to conciseness and precision of definitions in mathematics. Students need many opportunities to generate, analyze, and compare definitions for particular 2-D shapes. Additionally, students need help in developing an understanding of the nature and purpose of definitions in mathematics. The tasks in figure 3.8 can help you assess your students' understanding of these ideas and then facilitate discussion of them.

Knowledge of assessment

Writing can help students develop their understanding of mathematical concepts (Shepard 1993) and can also be highly useful to teachers for assessing students' understanding of mathematics (Pugalee 1997; Silver, Kilpatrick, and Schlesinger 1990). Furthermore, mathematical writing encompasses different genres. Marks and Mousley (1990) describe the following genres:

- Procedure—writing that tells how something is done

- Description—writing that tells what a particular thing is like

- Report—writing that tells what an entire class of things is like

- Explanation—writing that tells the reason why a judgment has been made

- Exposition—writing that presents arguments about why a thesis has been produced

This chapter has discussed some tasks that asked students to explain their thinking. It is important to help students develop writing competencies that are analogous to those that mathematicians use. Therefore, you need assessment tasks that require your students not only to describe how they solved mathematics problems but also to provide mathematical arguments, justify their thinking, and generalize beyond a small number of cases. Useful assessment questions to ask your students to assess their thinking include the following:

- "For what shape [or shapes] is this [a statement or a particular attribute or property] always true?"

- "Can you make a shape where this [an attribute or property] does hold?"

- "Can you make a shape where this [an attribute or property] does not hold?"

- "How do you know?"

- "Can you explain this in a different way?"

- "How are all of these shapes alike?"

- "How are these shapes different from one another?"

Responding to such questions will help students develop skill in using different genres of mathematics writing while at the same time providing you with opportunities to assess their level of skill and understanding.

Conclusion

As students mature in their geometric understanding from level 1 (Visual) to level 2 (Descriptive/Analytic), they begin to identify and describe shapes by their properties. When students develop an understanding of definitions and use these definitions to organize and classify shapes within a hierarchy, they begin to make the transition to level 3 (Abstract/Relational). Each student is likely to proceed at his or her own pace, and multiple activities and opportunities are needed to help all students develop an understanding of the attributes and definitions of shapes and relationships among shapes. Chapter 4 discusses common misconceptions that students have about the attributes of perimeter and area and strategies for clarifying their thinking.

Chapter 4
Measuring Area and Perimeter

Big Idea 2
One way to analyze and describe geometric objects, relationships among them, or the spaces they occupy is to quantify—measure or count—one or more of their attributes.

Essential Understanding 2a
Measurement can specify "how much" by assigning a number that corresponds to a chosen unit to such attributes as length, area, volume, and angle.

To function successfully in the world, students must understand the notion of measurement and the process of measuring. Students interact every day with quantities that provide a foundation on which, with help, they can build new knowledge and formalize their early understandings. For example, students gain a sense of how much a two-liter bottle holds, how heavy their backpacks are, how far they travel to school, and how warm or cold their classroom is. Measurement involves identifying an attribute on which to focus while ignoring other attributes that are present, as Lehrer and Slovin observe in *Developing Essential Understanding of Geometry and Measurement for Teaching Mathematics in Grades 3–5*. Measurement requires attending to the *volume* of water in the two-liter bottle, the *weight* of the backpack, the *distance* traveled to school, and the *temperature* of the classroom, to the exclusion of other attributes to which students might attend. This chapter focuses on ways to build on the informal or intuitive knowledge that students have acquired before grades 3–5 to develop a deeper understanding of area and perimeter.

Starting with the Attributes: Working toward Big Idea 2 and Essential Understanding 2*a*

In many ways, the most challenging part of measurement involves focusing on the desired attribute. Students may or may not attend to the attributes that they need to focus on to make a specific measurement. As you provide your students with various representations to help them to develop their understanding of perimeter and area, you may find that they do not attend to the attributes that you thought they would. Consider an introductory task, Brownie Decision, shown in figure 4.1. You might offer your students this task to help them think carefully about the different attributes that they could consider and what attributes they need to focus on to perform the task successfully.

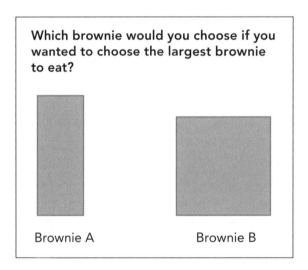

Fig. 4.1. Brownie Decision: An introductory task related to area and perimeter

For many students in grades 3–5, the Brownie Decision task may be difficult because they often attend to the longest dimension (Carpenter 1976): the brownie's "height" as represented in the diagram. Thus, many students choose brownie A over brownie B as the larger brownie. However, if students are asked to cover each brownie with cutout squares, they usually recognize that the region of brownie B is larger than the region of brownie A. Assuming that the thickness (depth) of the brownies is the same, brownie B would be larger than brownie A.

Tasks such as that in figure 4.1 can help students begin to consider various attributes that can be measured. Such tasks focus their attention on the underlying ideas of perimeter and area and help them recognize that area and perimeter have different attributes. However, many students and adults have a limited view of perimeter and area, often tied to formulas such as *Area = length × width*. They do not recognize that area involves determining a quantity of square units that will cover a region without gaps or overlaps or that perimeter is the distance around a region (Vighi and Marchini 2011). Focusing students on formulas rather than on the meaning of perimeter and area can lead to difficulty when students need to transfer ideas to new situations. For example, if students think area is always "length times width," they may not be able to find the area of a trapezoid and may have trouble retaining information, including various area formulas.

Measuring with attributes in mind

A focus on formulas rather than underlying mathematical ideas may in fact be one reason why students' performance in measurement is weaker than it is in other areas in the mathematics curriculum (Thompson and Preston 2004). For example, Martin and Strutchens (2000) note that on the seventh National Assessment of Educational Progress (NAEP), only 12 percent of students in grade 8 could determine the number of square tiles needed to cover a region of given dimensions.

As a teacher, you must think deeply about the attributes of area and perimeter yourself if you wish to help your students develop a robust understanding of these concepts and related processes. Reflect 4.1 turns your attention to these attributes, which may become clearer and more concrete if you think about them in relation to a particular shape, such as the irregular shape presented in figure 4.2.

Reflect 4.1

What attributes do you attend to when you examine the area and the perimeter of a particular figure?

Determine the perimeter and area of the irregular shape shown in figure 4.2, given that the distance between adjacent horizontal or vertical intersections shown inside the shape is one unit.

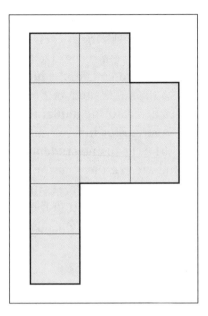

Fig. 4.2. An irregular shape, with the distance between adjacent horizontal or vertical intersections equal to one unit

To determine the area of the shape in figure 4.2 correctly, you had to count the number of unit squares, arriving at 10 square units (see fig. 4.3). To determine the perimeter of the shape correctly as 16 units, you needed to focus on the length of the sides (see fig. 4.4). Note that in the process of measuring, you used three steps that are described by Van de Walle, Karp, and Bay-Williams (2010, p. 376):

1. Decide on the attribute to be measured.

2. Select a unit that has that attribute.

3. Compare the units by filling, covering, matching, or using some other method, with the attribute of the object being measured. The number of units required is the measure.

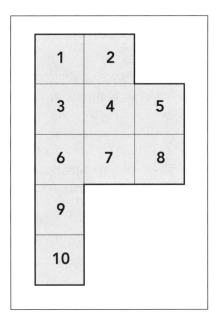

Fig. 4.3. Finding the area of the shape in figure 4.2 by counting the unit squares

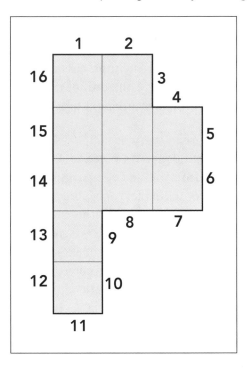

Fig. 4.4. Finding the perimeter of the shape in figure 4.2 by focusing on the lengths of the sides

Determining the area required you to recognize that you needed to focus on the *region* covered by the shape and count the number of square units *within the boundary* of the shape. In the case of the shape in figure 4.2, you did not need to fill or cover the shape, since the grid shown in the figure does this work for you. Determining the perimeter, by contrast, required you to recognize that you needed to consider the *length of the sides* of the shape and count the units *on the boundary* of the shape. Students often confuse the meanings of area and perimeter and use them interchangeably (Hart and Booth 1984). As later examples will illustrate, many difficulties that students have with area and perimeter are related to a shallow understanding of the meaning of these attributes.

Once students recognize and distinguish between the attributes of perimeter (that is, the *distance around* a shape) and area (that is, the *region inside* a shape), they can engage in measuring the area and perimeter of various shapes. For area, the standard process of measuring involves determining the number of square units that cover a region, though other, nonstandard units can also be used. Van de Walle, Karp, and Bay-Williams (2010) suggest offering various nonstandard shapes and beginning with nonstandard units and progressing to the use of standard units. The early use of nonstandard units focuses students' attention first on what it means to measure and prevents them from confounding this process with the size of a particular standard unit. Having students estimate a measurement before they engage in the third step of the measurement process is also important. Estimating allows students to gain a better sense of the unit of measure and directs their attention to what they will do in the measurement process.

Nevertheless, even something seemingly as simple as finding the distance around a figure can be challenging for students. As noted by Battista (2006), various strategies that students use for determining and comparing lengths may inhibit their understanding of perimeter. For example, some students may fail to maintain the same unit length when measuring an object. Other students may focus on counting the number of hash marks or dots rather than counting the number of iterations of the unit. This difficulty sometimes arises as students move from counting discrete objects to counting units that represent a continuous quantity—in this case, length. Discrete objects are naturally partitioned; length, by contrast, can be partitioned by any particular unit (Joram, Subrahmanyam, and Gelman 1998).

Similarly, students who use squares or square tiles to determine the perimeter of a shape may overcount or undercount if they focus on counting the number of squares on the perimeter or interior. Figures 4.5 and 4.6 show common counting errors. Students who correctly determine the perimeter must focus on the side length of the squares rather than the number of squares. Figures 4.7 and 4.8 show correct counting methods.

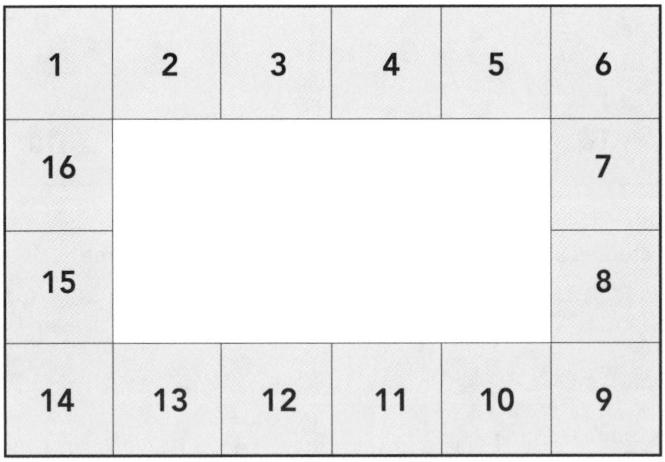

Fig. 4.5. A student's faulty process of counting interior squares to determine the perimeter of a rectangle

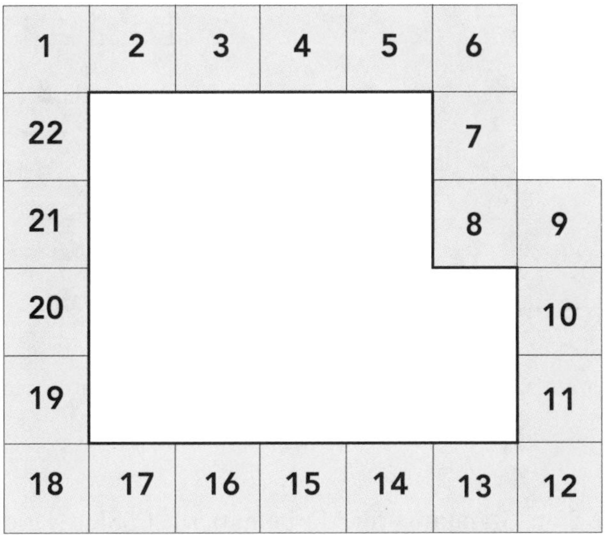

Fig. 4.6. A student's faulty process of counting exterior squares to determine the perimeter of a figure

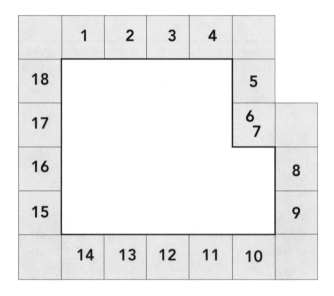

Fig. 4.7. A student's correct counting of sides of interior squares to determine the perimeter of a rectangle

Fig. 4.8. A student's correct counting of sides of exterior squares to determine the perimeter of a figure

The Common Core State Standards for Mathematics (CCSSM; National Governors Association Center for Best Practices and Council of Chief State School Officers 2010) emphasize the importance of solving problems involving area and perimeter, as shown in the grade 3 Measurement and Data standard related to perimeter, presented in figure 4.9.

Common Core State Standards for Mathematics, Grade 3

Measurement and Data

Geometric measurement: recognize perimeter as an attribute of plane figures and distinguish between linear and area measures.

8. Solve real world and mathematical problems involving perimeters of polygons, including finding the perimeter given the side lengths, finding an unknown side length, and exhibiting rectangles with the same perimeter and different areas or with the same area and different perimeters.

Fig. 4.9. Grade 3 content standard for solving problems involving perimeters of polygons. CCSSM 3.MD.8 (NGA Center and CCSSO 2010, p. 25).

One way to introduce students to perimeter is to present them with situations that are familiar and consequently facilitate connections with the concept. We developed the Puppy Fencing task, shown in figure 4.10, and gave it to 143 students in grades 3–5 to allow us to investigate how they used the context in approaching the situation. Note that we carefully designed this situation so that students had only the length and width of the area to be fenced and needed to determine the two missing sides. Examine the Puppy Fencing task while considering the question in Reflect 4.2

Reflect 4.2

How would you expect your students to perform on the Puppy Fencing task, shown in figure 4.10?

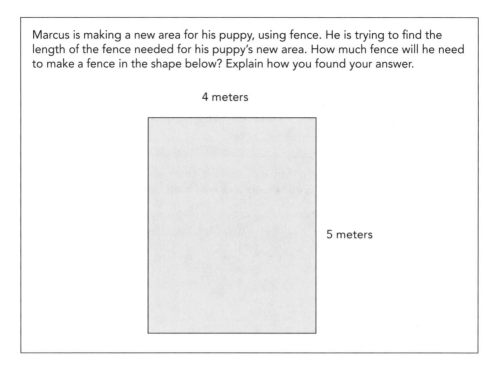

Marcus is making a new area for his puppy, using fence. He is trying to find the length of the fence needed for his puppy's new area. How much fence will he need to make a fence in the shape below? Explain how you found your answer.

4 meters

5 meters

Fig. 4.10. Puppy Fencing task

Figure 4.11 shows the performance of our students on this problem. Nearly three-quarters of the students in third grade correctly determined the perimeter of the figure, and about one-fifth of our third graders omitted the task. The two third-grade students (4.3%) who provided incorrect results wrote that they needed only 9 meters of fence, failing to calculate the fencing needed on the two unlabeled sides of the rectangle. Of the fourth- and fifth-grade students who responded incorrectly, almost all chose to multiply the two dimensions of the rectangle as though they were trying to determine the area of the figure.

	Grade 3 (47 students)	Grade 4 (48 students)	Grade 5 (48 students)
Correct	74.5%	63.2%	85.1%
Incorrect	4.3%	21.1%	14.9%
Omitted	21.3%	15.8%	0.0%

Fig. 4.11. Performance on the Puppy Fencing task by 143 students in grades 3–5

Ashlock (2006) noted that students often focus on superficial elements of a task. For example, when the lengths of two sides of a figure are given, students may multiply the dimensions, whereas when given the lengths of all sides of a figure, they are more likely to add. This evidence points to the narrow focus that some students have on such tasks rather than the deep understanding that they are expected to develop. The third-grade students demonstrated a high level of success on the task relative to the fourth- and fifth-grade students, who may have been focusing on patterns in the figure labels instead of reasoning about the situation and developing a deeper understanding of the meaning and use of perimeter and area.

Drawing on attributes to generate definitions

Helping students develop initial, informal definitions of area and perimeter that they can connect later with the formal definitions is important. Your students will construct meaning whether you share a formal definition with them or not. But they are more likely to develop a sense of the meaning of perimeter and area through various focused activities than by hearing definitions and being encouraged to memorize them. As noted by Tall and Vinner (1981), students develop a "concept image" of area and perimeter that is a combination of mental images and associated properties and actions.

All of this suggests the value of working intentionally to help students shape accurate meanings and informal definitions of these terms. Students must view perimeter as a distance—in particular, the distance around a closed 2-D figure. This perspective can grow out of and build on their prior experiences with length and measuring it in K–grade 2. However, as you help your students build on their earlier experiences with length to see perimeter as a distance, you must be careful when you introduce the concept of area, because area and the units for measuring it are quite different from perimeter and the units for measuring it.

Work with area is very different from students' prior work with length. Working with area requires coordinating lengths to form a region but attending to an attribute that is very different from length. This leads to difficulty for students as they try to build on their prior knowledge and experiences with length. Figure 4.12 shows definitions of area offered by fourth and fifth graders. Reflect 4.3 poses a question for you to consider in relation to these definitions and the definition of area that you present to your own students.

Reflect 4.3

Read the definitions of area presented in figure 4.12, written by fourth- and fifth-grade students.

What correct and incomplete understandings of area do these definitions demonstrate?

How are these definitions similar to or different from the definition that you present to your students?

Definition 1:	Area is the length × width of a shape.
Definition 2:	Area is the amount of space a shape takes, especially on flat surfaces.
Definition 3:	Area is a bunch of squares that you color in.
Definition 4:	Area is how big something is on the inside.
Definition 5:	Area is the cubic units inside of a 2-D shape.

Fig. 4.12. Definitions of area offered by fourth- and fifth-grade students

Many definitions of area offered by students demonstrate elements of correct thinking while also incorporating incorrect thinking. Definition 1 is a typical response that often comes from adults as well as schoolchildren, since adults frequently equate the meaning of area with a formula. However, this definition offers a very narrow view of area and relates only to rectangles. Definition 2 has many elements of a correct definition, since area is the measure of the space that is bounded by a 2-D shape. The student who wrote definition 2 included many of these characteristics. By contrast, the student who offered definition 3 appears to have confused a process that he had completed for measuring area with area itself. Although his definition suggests that measuring area involves ("a bunch of") squares, it does not focus on the measurement as the number of square units within the boundary of a 2-D shape. Definition 4 refers to a quantity and indicates the student's focus on measuring the interior of a region, although she could also be referring to a 3-D shape. Definition 5 includes conflicting information about 2-D and 3-D shapes. How cubic units could be arranged in a 2-D shape is unclear. This student may have had difficulty distinguishing between 2-D and 3-D shapes or may have focused on an activity in which he covered a 2-D region with 3-D shapes, such as cubes or square tiles. Overall, the goal is for students to recognize that area is the region inside a 2-D shape and is typically measured with squares.

Early tasks to apply and reinforce understanding

To develop a robust understanding of area, students need early opportunities to count and cover shapes with squares. Research has suggested that grasping the relationship between covering a region with concrete materials and working with the area formula is difficult for students (Doig, Cheeseman, and Lindsay 1995). Some materials, such as square tiles, appear to be too easy to use and obscure some of the underlying ideas. Some researchers suggest using paper squares to cover a surface to determine the area. Working with paper squares can focus students on the need to cover a surface completely without overlap or gaps. Current U.S. textbooks often present students with shapes that are already placed on a grid. Thus, when students determine the areas of these shapes, they do not need to recognize and apply the idea that the squares must not overlap or have gaps. The lack of challenge in such tasks may come at a cost. The impact that they have on a student's spatial structuring may not be great enough to foster the growth of a deep understanding of area. A useful strategy is to ask students initially to iterate squares inside a shape to determine the area, in this way encouraging them to consider the spatial structuring inside the area of a figure.

Regularly offering students perimeter and area tasks together helps them to compare and contrast the attributes to which these constructs require them to attend. To gain further insight into strategies for developing students' thinking about perimeter and area, consider the tasks in figures 4.13 and 4.14, which can be used together to lay a foundation for these ideas. Use the questions in Reflect 4.4 to help you consider the mathematical ideas that you can highlight through these tasks.

Reflect 4.4

Consider the paired measurement tasks on area and perimeter in figures 4.13 and 4.14.

What mathematical ideas do these tasks emphasize?

What ideas do students need to understand and apply to arrive at the correct result for these tasks?

How would you predict that your students would perform on these tasks?

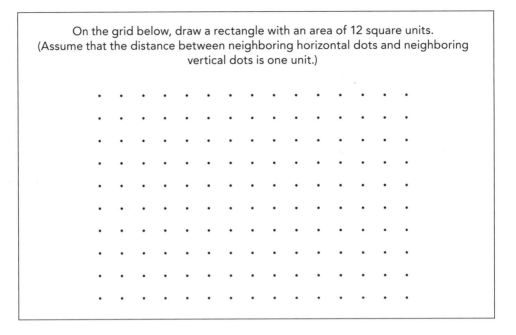

Fig. 4.13. Drawing task for area of a rectangle

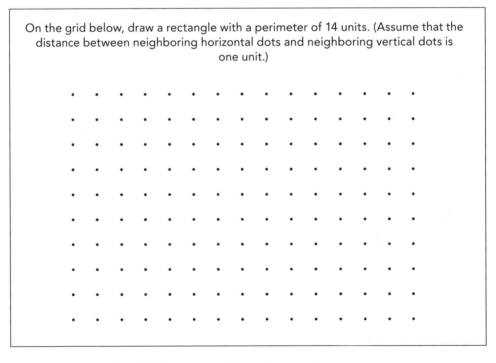

Fig. 4.14. Drawing task for perimeter of a rectangle

Paired tasks such as these can assist students in comparing and contrasting the attributes of area and perimeter. Students must recognize and apply the attributes of area and perimeter to complete the tasks successfully. As a later extension, students could be asked to create *all the possible* rectangles that have an area of 12 square units or a perimeter of 14 units. Furthermore, they could be asked to see whether they could create a particular rectangle—say, with an area of 24 square units and a perimeter of 22 units. Building a foundational understanding of the meaning of area as data is important; results from the 2003 NAEP suggest that fourth-grade students have a limited understanding of this topic (Blume, Galindo, and Walcott 2007).

We offered the tasks in figures 4.13 and 4.14 to 55 fourth- and fifth-grade students in three different classrooms, and a variety of student thinking emerged. Figures 4.15–4.20 show work that we received from four fifth graders and one fourth grader. Use the questions in Reflect 4.5 to guide your inspection of these samples of student work.

Reflect 4.5

Figures 4.15, 4.16, and 4.17 show work from three fifth graders, Tamara, Enrique, and Kathryn, respectively, on the area task shown in figure 4.13. Figures 4.18, 4.19, and 4.20 show work from a fourth grader, Evan, and two fifth graders, Micah, and Sarah, respectively, on the perimeter task in figure 4.14.

What understandings or misunderstandings do these samples of work suggest that the students might have had?

Consider some examples of work from students in your own classroom. What understandings or misunderstandings does this work reveal?

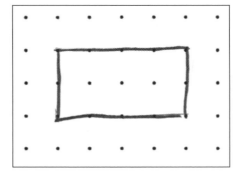

Fig. 4.15. Tamara's (grade 5) attempt to draw a rectangle with an area of 12 square units in response to the task shown in figure 4.13

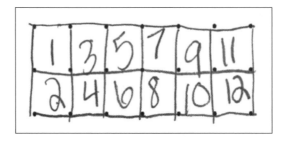

Fig. 4.16. Enrique's (grade 5) attempt to draw a rectangle with an area of 12 square units in response to the task shown in figure 4.13

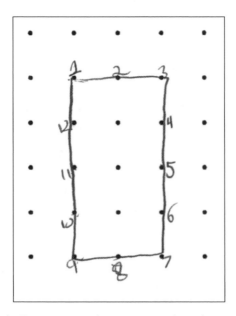

Fig. 4.17. Kathryn's (grade 5) attempt to draw a rectangle with an area of 12 square units in response to the task shown in figure 4.13

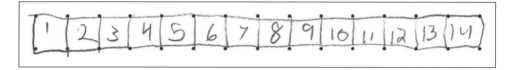

Fig. 4.18. Evan's (grade 4) attempt to draw a rectangle with perimeter of 14 units in response to the task shown in figure 4.14

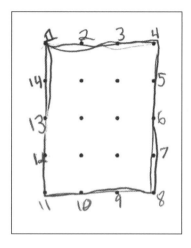

Fig. 4.19. Micah's (grade 5) attempt to draw a rectangle with perimeter of 14 units in response to the task shown in figure 4.14

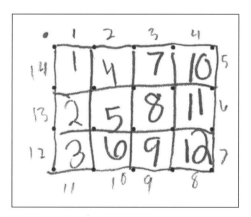

Fig. 4.20. Sarah's (grade 5) attempt to draw a rectangle with perimeter of 14 units in response to the task shown in figure 4.14

As shown in the samples of student work, the students who had difficulty demonstrated a misunderstanding of the attribute to be measured, and this misunderstanding prevented them from measuring the desired attribute successfully. Tamara (see fig. 4.15) drew a rectangle with a perimeter of 12 units rather than an area of 12 square units. Similarly, Evan (see fig. 4.18) drew a rectangle with an area of 14 square units rather than a perimeter of 14 units. The work from Kathryn (see fig. 4.17) and Micah (see fig. 4.19) shows that they counted the number of dots on the grid instead of the number of squares (in the case of area) or the lengths of the sides (in the case of perimeter). Enrique (see fig. 4.16) and Sarah (see fig. 4.20) attended to the correct attributes. Activities such as these can support students in contrasting area and perimeter—particularly when their work is reinforced by classroom discussions that focus their attention on various correct and incorrect responses that surface in students' work. Sharing examples of work that shows these common errors and purportedly comes from fictitious students "in other classrooms" can also help dispel your own students' confusion and clarify their thinking.

Composing and decomposing to investigate measurements

Students should also investigate and compare the areas of noncongruent shapes to develop a better understanding of the connection of area and perimeter with the units in which they are measured. Composition and decomposition can be valuable in this work. For example, consider how students could compare different shapes that have the same area, such as those in figure 4.21.

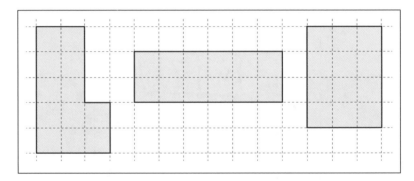

Fig. 4.21. Students can compare the areas of noncongruent shapes that have the same area.

Such activities can also help students recognize that while shapes that are congruent have the same shape and size, shapes that are not congruent may nevertheless have the same area. Working on grid paper, students could also draw three noncongruent triangles that have the same height and base (see fig. 4.22) and make conjectures about how the areas compare. The students could then cut and rearrange the parts to see that these three triangles have the same area. Eventually, of course, students will be expected to understand that these triangles have the same area without actually calculating the area of each one.

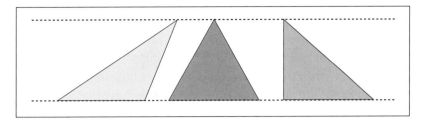

Fig. 4.22. Students can compare the areas of triangles that have the same base and height.

Students often have difficulty recognizing that the area may remain the same when a shape changes in a way that conserves its area (Carpenter et al. 1975). Many eight- or nine-year-olds do not understand that rearranging areas into different shapes does not affect the overall area (Piaget, Inhelder, and Szeminska 1960), a finding that underscores the importance of providing opportunities for students to compose and decompose shapes. For example, you might give your students a parallelogram like that in figure 4.23 and ask them to use scissors to cut off the right triangle (with the height of 2 units and base of 2 units) from the parallelogram's left side. You could then tell them to move it to the parallelogram's right side to create a rectangle with a length of 4 units and height of 2 units. This work may help them understand that the initial parallelogram and the newly created rectangle have the same area. Students need many opportunities to partition and rearrange shapes without changing the area.

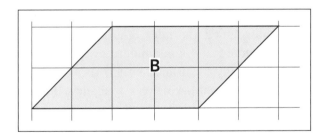

Fig. 4.23. Parallelogram B can be partitioned and rearranged to make a rectangle.

On a related note, students need to recognize that a square unit counted in a measurement need not be an intact square but could be in parts that have various shapes put together to constitute a square unit. For example, they may have two halves of a square unit that are "left over" but need to be counted as part of the area (see the shaded regions in fig. 4.24, for instance). Because these do not appear in the visible form of a square, some students may not recognize them as constituting a square unit in the area of the shape. This misconception may be fostered by the way in which the students think of "square unit" or the definition for it that they have encountered. For example, some textbooks define a square unit as a square with sides that are each one unit long rather than as the interior of a shape that has the same area as a square with sides that are one unit long. It is important to recognize that a single task or activity will not shift the thinking of all students in your classroom. Returning to related activities that highlight these ideas is essential so that you can continue to confront misconceptions that your students have about area.

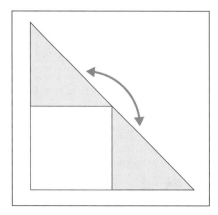

Fig. 4.24. An example of two partial square units that make a whole square unit

Developing spatial structuring and making connections to multiplication and the area formula

After your students have developed an understanding of the meaning of area and perimeter by using both standard and nonstandard units, including various irregular shapes, they will be ready to formalize their thinking and develop general procedures for finding the areas and perimeters of shapes. However, as they acquire skill in using various strategies to determine the area or perimeter of a figure, you should be sure that they do not lose sight of the connection that they have made to the meaning of area and perimeter. A focus on reasoning about ways to determine the area of rectangles aligns with the primary focus of the Common Core Standards in grade 3, as shown in figure 4.25.

Common Core State Standards for Mathematics, Grade 3

Measurement and Data

Geometric measurement: understand concepts of area and relate area to multiplication and to addition.

5. Recognize area as an attribute of plane figures and understand concepts of area measurement.

   a. A square with side length 1 unit, called "a unit square," is said to have "one square unit" of area, and can be used to measure area.

   b. A plane figure which can be covered without gaps or overlaps by *n* unit squares is said to have an area of *n* square units.

6. Measure areas by counting unit squares (square cm, square m, square in, square ft, and improvised units).

7. Relate area to the operations of multiplication and addition.

   a. Find the area of a rectangle with whole-number side lengths by tiling it, and show that the area is the same as would be found by multiplying the side lengths.

   b. Multiply side lengths to find areas of rectangles with whole-number side lengths in the context of solving real world and mathematical problems, and represent whole-number products as rectangular areas in mathematical reasoning.

   c. Use tiling to show in a concrete case that the area of a rectangle with whole-number side lengths a and $b + c$ is the sum of $a \times b$ and $a \times c$. Use area models to represent the distributive property in mathematical reasoning.

   d. Recognize area as additive. Find areas of rectilinear figures by decomposing them into non-overlapping rectangles and adding the areas of the non-overlapping parts, applying this technique to solve real world problems.

Geometry

Reason with shapes and their attributes.

2. Partition shapes into parts with equal areas. Express the area of each part as a unit fraction of the whole. *For example, partition a shape into 4 parts with equal area, and describe the area of each part as $^1/_4$ of the area of the shape.*

Fig. 4.25. Grade 3 content standards related to working with area.
CCSSM 3.MD.5–7; 3.G.2 (NGA Center and CCSSO 2010, pp. 25–26).

Initially, students should use squares to determine the area of rectangles. Van de Walle, Karp, and Bay-Williams (2010) suggest that the focus of these initial activities be on the meaning of multiplication and how it can be used to determine the area of rectangles. Later, the focus can be shifted to developing a general formula for all rectangles. The distinction here is an important but difficult one. Students in grades 3–5 are also developing their understanding of the meaning of the operations of multiplication and division. A rush to the use of a formula without investigating the meaning of multiplication is likely to lead to a diminished understanding of both the operation and area for some students (Lannin, Chval, and Jones 2013).

Depending on the curricular materials that you use in your classroom, your students may be introduced to "length times width" or "base times height" for the area of a rectangle. The "base times height" terminology can be confusing to students, but "base" and "height" have clear mathematical meanings that apply to other shapes (for example, a parallelogram). Placing emphasis on "base times height" and connecting its use to ways of finding the area of other figures can be valuable.

The development of a deep understanding of the area of a rectangle depends on two attributes of spatial structuring, which is the mental arrangement of spatial objects (Battista 2006). First, spatial structuring typically allows recognition of a geometric relationship. Second, it lends support to important connections with a multiplicative relationship (Outhred and Mitchelmore 2004). Consider the spatial structuring required for understanding area. Students must coordinate rows and columns of an array as they consider the number of square units needed to cover a 2-D surface. As simple as this task may seem to adults, it is not automatic for students in grades 3–5.

To investigate the challenges that spatial structuring presents, we gave third-grade students the Structuring the Rectangle task shown in figure 4.26. This task showed students a rectangle with square tiles already filling two dimensions and asked them to finish filling it and determine the total number of square tiles.

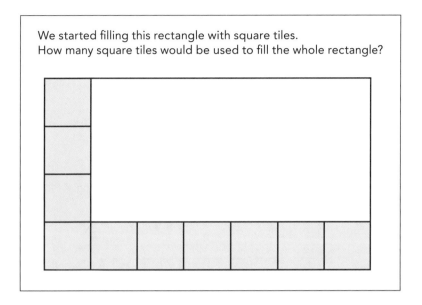

We started filling this rectangle with square tiles.
How many square tiles would be used to fill the whole rectangle?

Fig. 4.26. Structuring the Rectangle, a task designed to show students' spatial structuring for the area of a rectangle

To be successful with the task, the students had to coordinate the rows and columns of an array. Examine the samples of student work in figures 4.27–4.30. Let the questions in Reflect 4.6 guide you as you explore how students' coordination of the rows and columns may vary.

Reflect 4.6

Figures 4.27, 4.28, 4.29, and 4.30 present work by four third graders, Jaron, Samantha, Marissa, and Devin, respectively, on the Structuring the Rectangle task shown in figure 4.26.

What misunderstandings and understandings can you identify in the students' work?

What is your evidence for these misunderstandings and understandings?

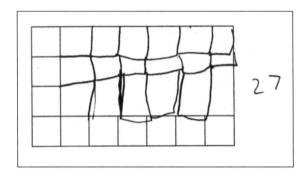

Fig. 4.27. Jaron's (grade 3) structuring of the rectangle

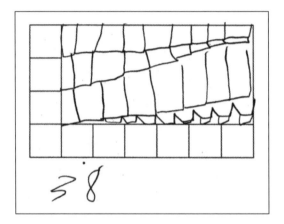

Fig. 4.28. Samantha's (grade 3) structuring of the rectangle

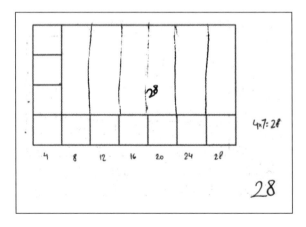

Fig. 4.29. Marissa's (grade 3) structuring of the rectangle

Fig. 4.30. Devin's (grade 3) structuring of the rectangle

Jaron (see fig. 4.27) demonstrated some understanding of the structure of an array but appears to have lacked some understanding of coordinating rows and columns, since his rows and columns were not the same size. Samantha (see fig. 4.28) had more difficulty coordinating the rows and columns. Her work offers an example of what Outhred and Mitchelmore (2000) refer to as an "incomplete covering" of such an array. In similar fashion, other third-grade students left gaps or added unnecessary rows or columns. Marissa (see fig. 4.29) demonstrated a deeper understanding of an array and also appears to have recognized the unit structure of 7 groups of 4, as evidenced by her skip-counting below each column, although she writes 4 × 7 = 28. Later discussion will revisit this type of reasoning to probe the connection between an array and the meaning of multiplication. In contrast, Devin (see fig. 4.30) coordinated the rows and columns appropriately, but the manner in which he counted the interior squares demonstrates that he had not made the connection with multiplication that Marissa recognized.

Tasks that promote the development of this spatial structuring will help your students in their initial attempts to determine the area of rectangles. Such tasks should precede the introduction of the general rules for area or else students will have little or no understanding of the meaning of area or the area formula. The tasks in figures 4.31 and 4.32 are additional sample activities that require students to fill in the interior of a rectangle with squares of a given unit.

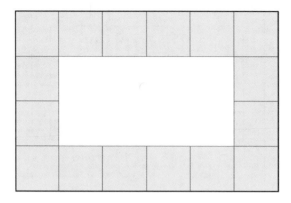

Fig. 4.31. A task promoting spatial structuring: students fill in the missing squares in a rectangle

Fig. 4.32. Students fill in the missing squares in a spatial structuring task that is more challenging than that in figure 4.31.

Discussion of such tasks can help students begin to recognize the consistent structure of an array. Such representations are an important part of building student understanding of area. However, many U.S. textbooks do not encourage student investigation to build understanding and develop spatial structuring prior to focusing on ways to determine the area of a rectangle. Many textbooks simply overlay a rectangle with a grid and point out that the area could be found by multiplying the length and the width.

Remember, just because your students can use the area formula for rectangles correctly, you should not conclude that they understand the meaning of area or have developed the spatial structuring necessary for that understanding. McCool and

Holland (2012) provide the example of Isaac, a fifth-grade student who correctly used a formula to find the area of a rectangle but did not demonstrate understanding supported by spatial structuring. Figure 4.33 shows Isaac's array for a rectangle.

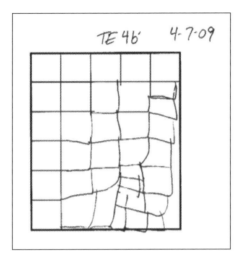

Fig. 4.33. Isaac's (grade 5) attempt to fill in the squares in a rectangle

Working with students to build a foundational understanding of the spatial structuring of an array of squares in a rectangle *prior to* helping them see a general relationship or develop a formula for area is important. Students' mental images and sense of the array structure are critical for developing deep understanding (Battista 2007). Without this foundation, they will have little understanding of the meaning of area. Transferring their knowledge to situations involving the area of triangles, parallelograms, or trapezoids will be difficult, as will be finding the volume of 3-D shapes. Battista (2006) notes that students who can identify a particular square in an array (say, finding the square in the third row and fourth column) have developed the spatial structuring necessary to begin connecting the meaning of multiplication with the structure of an array.

Once your students properly recognize and apply the spatial structuring of an array, you should help them connect their arrays to an efficient strategy for determining the number of squares in an array. To do this, students need to identify a multiplicative unit (Lannin, Chval, and Jones 2013; Outhred and Mitchelmore 2004)—either a row or a column—and determine the number of iterations that are required of that unit. For example, in figure 4.29 Marissa created a new unit—a multiplicative unit—of length 4. She recognized that the entire array could be thought of as consisting of groups of this length-4 unit. She then determined the number of multiplicative units of length 4—in this case, 7. She skip-counted 4, 8, 12, 16, 20, 24, 28 and recorded the number of squares as 4 × 7 = 28. Typically, we think of such a multiplication expression as indicating the multiplier first and the size of the multiplicative unit second. Thus, we would usually write 7 × 4 as an expression for the total number of squares needed to cover the surface of the rectangle. Alternatively, we could view a row as a multiplicative unit of length 7, as illustrated by the shaded row in figure 4.34, and recognize that we have 4 iterations of this length-7 unit, resulting in the expression 4 × 7 for the total number of squares.

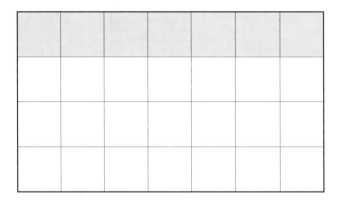

Fig. 4.34. A 4-by-7 array using 7 as the multiplicative unit

Generalizing the area formula and then revisiting the relationship between area and perimeter

By building your students' understanding of array structure, you can extend their understanding of the meaning of multiplication and connect it with the process of finding the area of any rectangle. After building their spatial structuring through activities in which they work with arrays and use multiplication to determine the number of squares in an array, you will have laid the groundwork for the critical question: "How could you find the area of *any* rectangle?"

One approach at this point is to have students examine and determine the area of various rectangles presented on grid paper. They will quickly notice that they can multiply the length and the width to determine the number of squares in any rectangle. However, a few words of caution are in order.

First, students' views of what it means to refer to a shape as a *rectangle* may be limited (see Chapters 1 and 3). Adults may have a broad and dynamic view of this shape, but students might not. Encouraging them to explain and demonstrate what they mean by a rectangle is important. In fact, NAEP results provide evidence that some students in the United States lack the necessary conceptual connections for full understanding of a rectangle and its area. For example, NAEP items for grade 7 students revealed that students at this level could calculate the area of a rectangle when given both dimensions. However, when these students were given the length of one side and asked to find the area of a square, only 13 percent applied their knowledge of the area formula—although most of them knew that the sides of a square are equal (Carpenter et al. 1988). Thus, students may not transfer their knowledge of finding the area of rectangles to rectangles that are squares. Targeting finding the area of a square and treating it as a special case of finding the area of a rectangle are important. However, some textbooks provide different formulas for rectangles and squares. This differentiation is unnecessary and can be detrimental to student learning, since it does not recognize that a square is a special case of a rectangle.

Second, students may not understand the extent to which the length-times-width formula for the area of a rectangle can be applied. Questioning them about its application is important. For example, you might ask your students, "Can the formula *length × width = Area* be applied to situations where the side lengths are not whole numbers?" Do they think that it would work for a rectangle of length 3.5 centimeters and width 4 centimeters, for instance? Students should persuade themselves that this process permits finding the area for any rectangle, with any side lengths.

Third, students often develop generalizations about perimeter and area that may or may not be true. After working with your students to develop the concept of, and formula for, the area of a rectangle, returning to contrasting perimeter and area can be helpful. Consider the task presented in figure 4.35, for example. We gave this task (similar to one used by Ma [1999]), to 86 fourth- and fifth-grade students. Use the questions in Reflect 4.7 to focus your thinking about the task.

Reflect 4.7

The task shown in figure 4.35 presents Brian, a student who has an idea about a relationship between perimeter and area. Read the task, and consider how you would respond to Brian's claim.

How would you expect your students to respond to it?

How would you explain why Brian's claim is or is not true?

> Brian looked at two rectangles, rectangle A and rectangle B. The perimeter of rectangle A is greater than the perimeter of rectangle B. Brian said, "The area of rectangle A must be greater than the area of rectangle B." Do you agree with Brian? Why or why not?

Fig. 4.35. A task asking students to evaluate Brian's thinking.
Based on Ma (1999, p. 84).

This task can provoke some deep thinking about the relationship between perimeter and area. Further, it requires students to consider how they can validate or invalidate the claim that Brian made. In approaching the task, you may have begun by drawing various rectangles and considering the areas and perimeters of these rectangles. Perhaps you found a counterexample, such as a 4-by-5 rectangle (area of 20 square units and perimeter of 18 units) and a 1-by-10 rectangle (area of 10 square units and perimeter of 22 units). Such a counterexample would demonstrate that Brian's claim is false. In fact, an infinite number of examples exist that support Brian's claim, and an infinite number of examples could be found that show that Brian's claim is false. However, only one counterexample is necessary to show that this general statement is false (Lannin, Ellis, and Elliot 2011).

This task, as you might imagine, is challenging for both adults and students. The results of our work with fourth- and fifth-grade students appear in figure 4.36.

	Student Responses		
	Brian was correct	Brian was incorrect	Omitted
Fourth grade (38 students)	63.2%	10.5%	26.3%
Fifth grade (48 students)	75.0%	25.0%	0.0%

Fig. 4.36. Results for fourth- and fifth-grade students on Brian's conjecture

Despite the difficulty of this task, 25 percent of our fifth-grade students and 10.5 percent of our fourth-grade students recognized that Brian's conjecture was incorrect and provided a strong explanation of why it was incorrect. Of the students who recognized that Brian was incorrect, the majority provided a single counterexample.

For instance, Maria, whose work appears in figure 4.37, noted that Brian's statement is not always true and provided the counterexample of a 6-by-1 rectangle and a 3-by-3 rectangle. In contrast to Maria and the other students who offered a single counterexample to show that Brian's claim is false, a number of students offered a single example in support of the claim. Figure 4.38 shows the work of one such student, Kayley, who increased one side length by 1 (from a 1-by-2 rectangle to a 1-by-3 rectangle) and concluded that this example demonstrated Brian's claim for all cases. Other students tried to draw on general relationships without examining specific cases. Sam, whose work is shown in figure 4.39, was one such student.

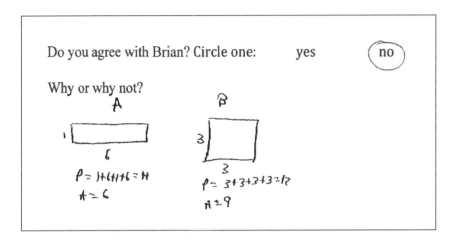

Fig. 4.37. Maria's (grade 5) counterexample to support her conclusion that Brian's conjecture is false

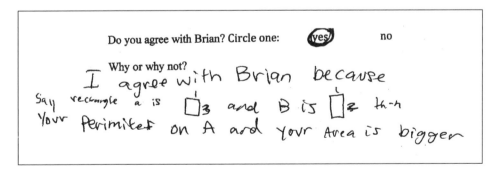

Fig. 4.38. Kayley's (grade 5) example to support her conclusion that Brian's conjecture is true

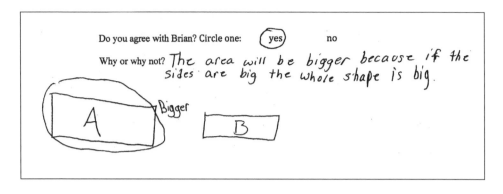

Fig. 4.39. Sam's (grade 5) support for his conclusion that Brian's conjecture is true

The work produced by Sam and Kayley indicates that both students needed additional time to investigate Brian's conjecture and discuss their ideas with other students. Kayley's response may suggest that she had other misconceptions about how a general statement can be shown to be true. Finding a few examples that fit a conjecture does not mean that the conjecture is true for all instances. By contrast, Sam seems to have considered various situations and arrived at what might appear to be a reasonable conclusion. However, he did not consider all possibilities either and might have benefited from examining other cases.

Figure 4.40 illustrates an extension task that can offer students a different opportunity to consider the relationship between area and perimeter. In the example shown, a nonstandard geometric shape has been created with fourteen square tiles. Students then place an additional square tile adjacent to one of the existing tiles and consider the impact of the added tile on the area and the perimeter. Alternatively, students might move one of the existing square tiles, placing it adjacent to different tiles making up the original shape and consider how the perimeter and area change depending on where the tile is placed (fig. 4.41 shows one example). The goal is to make explicit to students the idea that different geometric shapes can have the same areas but different perimeters, as shown by the moving of an existing tile in figure 4.41, or the same perimeters but different areas, as shown by the addition of a tile in figure 4.40.

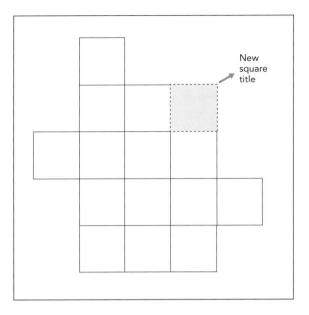

Fig. 4.40. A task for examining the impact of adding a tile on the area and perimeter of a figure

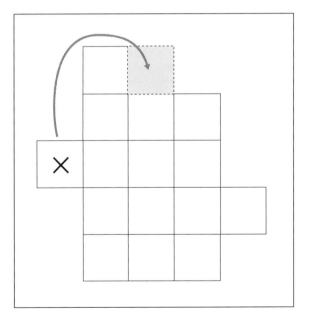

Fig. 4.41. A situation for examining the impact of moving a tile on the perimeter and area of a figure

One final note to consider as you work to build your students' understanding of area in grades 3–5: Remember, determining area actually involves calculating the area of the *region in the interior* of a figure. The term *rectangle* refers to the sides and the vertices, not the interior region bounded by the rectangle. Thus, speaking of "finding the area of a rectangle" may be confusing to students, who need to focus on finding the area of the region inside the rectangle. This clarification can help address students' misunderstanding about the attribute that they are measuring when they find the area. Rather than addressing perimeter separately with all activities, strategically interweaving activities that allow students to compare and contrast perimeter and area throughout instruction can help students distinguish between a rectangle and the region inside it.

Summarizing Pedagogical Content Knowledge to Support Big Idea 2 and Essential Understanding 2*a*

Teaching the mathematical ideas in this chapter requires specialized knowledge related to the four components presented in the Introduction: learners, curriculum, instructional strategies, and assessment. The four sections that follow summarize some examples of these specialized knowledge bases in relation to Big Idea 2 and, in particular, Essential Understanding 2*a* in the case of area and perimeter. Although we separate them to highlight their importance, we also recognize that they are connected and support one another.

Knowledge of learners

This chapter has highlighted different student misconceptions that may surface as you pose problems related to area and perimeter. Battista (2006) described student strategies for determining and comparing lengths that may inhibit students' understanding of perimeter. For example, some students may fail to maintain the same unit length when measuring an object. Other students may focus on counting the number of hash marks or dots rather than counting the number of iterations of the unit to determine the perimeter. Students tend to focus on counting discrete objects rather than on measuring continuous quantities. They may think that if they rearrange given areas into different shapes, the overall area changes (Piaget, Inhelder, and Szeminska 1960). Anticipating these misconceptions will help guide the design of lessons, questions, and assessments.

Knowledge of curriculum

Too often textbooks in grades 3–5 do not devote sufficient attention to develop the deep understanding of area and perimeter that students build through multiple investigations (see figs. 4.22 and 4.24, for example). As a result, students like Isaac (see fig. 4.33) may be able to use a formula correctly to find the area of a rectangle without having mastered the spatial structure of an array for a rectangle (McCool and Holland 2012). Or students may assume that when they are given the length and width of a rectangle, they should multiply them to find the answer, even if the question requires them to find the perimeter.

If you were to map the tasks in your curricular materials to the Common Core State Standards related to area and perimeter, what would you find? Would you find worthwhile tasks that are carefully sequenced to help students build their understanding of the meaning of attributes and units of measure and provide opportunities for students to develop spatial structuring and formulas? Would you find some images or shapes that include a grid overlay and others that invite students to cover shapes with squares? Do your curricular materials include irregular shapes such as that in figure 4.2 or arrays with some of the grid removed, such as those in figures 4.26, 4.31, and 4.32? Do your materials provide shapes oriented in various ways to help students recognize that the orientation of a figure does not change the area of the figure?

Knowledge of instructional strategies

Teachers can draw on many and varied instructional strategies in helping their students develop their understanding of area and perimeter. We highlight two examples here.

In initial work in determining the area of rectangles, students need tasks that promote the development of spatial structuring before they encounter the general rules for area. Otherwise, area and the area formula will have little or no meaning for them. Asking students to create different shapes by using cutout squares or grid paper can facilitate their development of spatial structuring and help them to make sense of the array structure.

Possibilities for helping students build a robust understanding of area and perimeter include giving them a dozen or so squares to create different shapes with the same area while discovering that some of these shapes have different perimeters. Students might also use a piece of wire or a pipe cleaner to create shapes that have different areas but the same perimeter.

Knowledge of assessment

Battista (2006) notes that students who can identify a particular square in an array— finding the square in the third row and fourth column, for example—have developed the spatial structuring necessary to begin connecting the meaning of multiplication with array structure. Therefore, assessing whether students can identify specific squares in arrays in this manner is very important.

As shown in figure 4.39 or some of the definitions in figure 4.12, students may overgeneralize. Therefore, it is important to include assessment items that will highlight these ideas so that they can be challenged. Some of the definitions in figure 4.12 demonstrate that students sometimes thought that "length times width" would give the area of any shape. Providing opportunities for students to write "definitions" or descriptions or asking them whether they agree or disagree with a fictitious student (see Reflect 4.7) can be productive assessment strategies that highlight students' overgeneralizations or misconceptions.

Conclusion

This chapter has discussed instructional strategies for building a robust under-standing of perimeter and area. Developing such understanding takes time, since students must connect their calculations of perimeter and area with representations that promote an understanding of the meaning of the proper attributes. The chapter has also shared particular misconceptions that your students are likely to have and that you need to assess, address, and dispel through targeted instructional activi-ties and corresponding discussions. Developing students' understanding of the meaning of perimeter and area takes considerable time, as the chapter has empha-sized, and current textbooks often fail to provide such opportunities for building understanding that students can carry forward and extend to other topics, includ-ing volume, which is the focus of the next chapter.

practice

Chapter 5
Understanding the Volume of
Rectangular Prisms

Big Idea 2
One way to analyze and describe geometric objects, relationships among them, or the spaces they occupy is to quantify—measure or count—one or more of their attributes.

Essential Understanding 2a
Measurement can specify "how much" by assigning a number that corresponds to a chosen unit to such attributes as length, area, volume, and angle.

Students need to understand area and perimeter before they begin to examine volume. This chapter focuses on ways to support them in understanding volume while building naturally on the concepts of area and perimeter and the strategies for developing students' understanding of them discussed in Chapter 4. Understanding the structure of arrays is critical to students, for example, as are recognizing the relationship of array structure to area measurement and connecting this relationship with the meaning of multiplication (Battista 2012a, 2012b). However, developing a deep understanding of volume is complex, and even students who draw on their intuitions and understanding related to length and area are likely to experience challenges as they seek to develop an understanding of volume and apply it in various situations. This chapter focuses specifically on work with the volume of rectangular prisms, since this work is emphasized in the Common Core State Standards (National Governors Association Center for Best Practices and Council of Chief State School Officers [NGA Center and CCSSO] 2010). As in the previous chapter, the underlying ideas in this chapter are Big Idea 2 and, in particular, Essential Understanding 2a, as identified in *Developing Essential Understanding of Geometry and Measurement for Teaching Mathematics in Grades 3–5* (Lehrer and Slovin 2014).

Focusing on the 3-D Space inside a Shape: Working toward Big Idea 2 and Essential Understanding 2*a*

What comes to mind when you think about volume? What volume activities do you recall working on when you were a student in elementary school or middle school? If you are like many adults, you may remember approaching volume through a formula. You may recall the formula for the volume of a rectangular prism as *Volume = length × width × height* and may remember using it to perform numerous calculations. Two points are important to recognize about this view of volume:

1. The formula *Volume = length × width × height* is correct for the volume of rectangular prisms but incorrect for the volumes of other 3-D shapes (triangular prisms, spheres, cylinders, and pyramids, for example).

2. Volume is not a formula but is typically viewed as the amount of three-dimensional space that a shape takes up (Van de Walle, Karp, and Bay-Williams 2010).

Considered as the amount of 3-D space occupied by a shape, volume is closely linked to capacity—that is, the amount that a 3-D container can hold. This chapter suggests using tasks that involve capacity to build students' understanding of volume. Volume is often measured in cubic units—the number of cubes of a uniform size needed to fill a 3-D space. Adults typically hear about volume as cubic space when buying a refrigerator (which might advertise 20 cubic feet of storage space) or a car (which might promise 110 cubic feet of cargo room). By contrast, many references to volume or capacity involve the use of units (gallons, liters, etc.) that do not refer explicitly to three dimensions, although the fact that they are units of volume implies that they do.

Volume can be determined for standard shapes quickly by using formulas. However, students in grades 3–5 initially have little understanding of volume even if they can use the formulas correctly (Battista 2007). Thus, considerable instructional effort should be devoted to developing and deepening students' understanding of the meaning of volume. Too often, students are introduced to formulas for volume before they have grasped what volume is or have developed the spatial structuring necessary to make sense of the formulas. Therefore, they are unlikely to be able to apply formulas appropriately in nonstandard contexts (Battista 2007) or in situations other than those that involve direct calculations of volume. Students who can correctly apply formulas to arrive at the correct value for the volume may have little understanding of what is being measured or why the formulas work. This chapter discusses strategies for deepening student understanding of volume.

Piaget (1965) demonstrated that children between the ages of 4 and 12 often have difficulty determining that the volumes of two different-looking containers may be the same. Piaget's most famous task, the Conservation of Liquid task, involved showing a child two identical containers that contained the same amount of liquid. The child was asked whether the two containers had the same amount of liquid. Once the child confirmed that they did, the liquid from one of the containers was poured into a taller, thinner container. The child was then asked whether the two containers still held the same amount of liquid. Children often said that the taller container had more, apparently because they focused on the attribute of height rather than the capacity of the container. The goal of work with children in grades 3–5 is to help them recognize that determining the volume of a shape involves more than attending to a single dimension. Instead, as they gradually learn, determining a shape's volume requires coordinating its length, width, and height. Figure 5.1 details a portion of the important ideas related to volume that the Common Core State Standards (CCSSM; NGA Center and CCSSO 2010) expects students in grade 5 to develop. Note that CCSSM emphasizes gaining an understanding of the meaning of volume and connecting volume with multiplication.

Common Core State Standards for Mathematics, Grade 5

Geometric measurement: understand concepts of volume and relate volume to multiplication and to addition.

3. Recognize volume as an attribute of solid figures and understand concepts of volume measurement.

    a. A cube with side length 1 unit, called a "unit cube," is said to have "one cubic unit" of volume, and can be used to measure volume.

    b. A solid figure which can be packed without gaps or overlaps using n unit cubes is said to have a volume of n cubic units.

4. Measure volumes by counting unit cubes, using cubic cm, cubic in, cubic ft, and improvised units.

5. Relate volume to the operations of multiplication and addition and solve real world and mathematical problems involving volume.

    a. Find the volume of a right rectangular prism with whole-number side lengths by packing it with unit cubes, and show that the volume is the same as would be found by multiplying the edge lengths, equivalently by multiplying the height by the area of the base. Represent threefold whole-number products as volumes, e.g., to represent the associative property of multiplication.

Fig. 5.1. A portion of the Common Core State Standards for volume in grade 5. CCSSM 5.MD.3–5 (NGA Center and CCSSO 2010, p. 37).

A useful way to build an initial understanding of cubic units and to begin having students think about volume is to engage them in activities that explore two supporting topics: (a) how much space a cube of a particular size occupies, and (b) how to build a 3-D shape from a 2-D representation of that shape. To investigate the first topic, students can build various shapes, with some students building shapes that are 1, 10, and 100 cubic centimeters and others building shapes that are 1, 10, and 100 cubic inches, as well as 1 cubic foot. Students could then estimate how many of these various cubes they would need to fill smaller containers.

Exploring the second topic helps students develop their sense of 3-D shapes. Students could build shapes with cubes to match 2-D diagrams of those shapes. For example, students could use cubic centimeters to build the 3-D shapes pictured in diagrams like those in figure 5.2. Students might compare and discuss the various arrangements and "missing" cubes that are not visible in the 2-D diagram. It is important that they consider cubes that exist but are not easily viewed in the diagram.

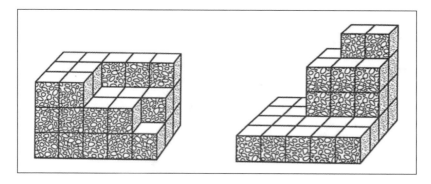

Fig. 5.2. Two-dimensional diagrams of three-dimensional objects. From Page, Wagreich, and Chval (1993c, p. 54).

Once students have developed an initial understanding of the relative sizes of various cube arrangements and have investigated the construction of various 3-D cube models, they will be ready for further investigations of ways to determine the volume of a rectangular prism. Throughout their work with volume, students need to connect 2-D diagrams, 3-D representations of volume, and symbolic representations of their volume calculations. Knowing how students view 2-D and 3-D representations is often difficult, so posing questions is important. One useful question is, "How did you decide where to put each cube?" Or, pointing to a particular cube in a 2-D drawing, you might ask, "Where is this in your 3-D model?"

Before delving more deeply into a consideration of volume and how an understanding of volume develops, take time to inspect the activity for students shown in figure 5.3 and respond to the questions in Reflect 5.1.

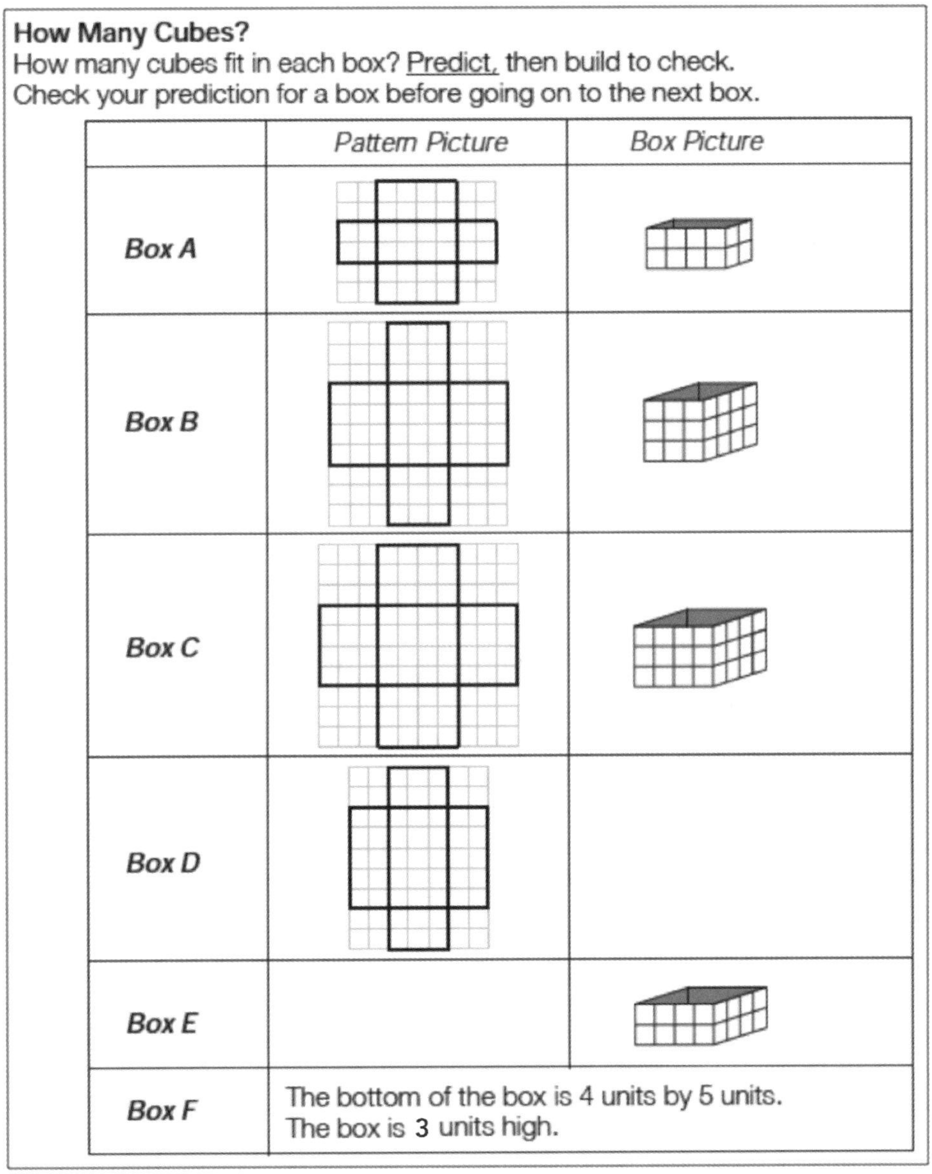
How Many Cubes?
How many cubes fit in each box? Predict, then build to check.
Check your prediction for a box before going on to the next box.

	Pattern Picture	*Box Picture*
Box A		
Box B		
Box C		
Box D		
Box E		
Box F	The bottom of the box is 4 units by 5 units. The box is 3 units high.	

Fig. 5.3. Volume investigation task. From Battista (1999, p. 421).

The activity in figure 5.3 presents students with a group of "pattern pictures" and "box pictures" for boxes that will hold different numbers of cubes. Examine the activity, and then consider the following questions:

What mathematical ideas would students need to recognize and apply to complete the task successfully?

How would you anticipate that your students would respond to the task?

What wrong answers would you anticipate?

Why would students be likely to give those wrong answers?

How would you want your students to view the arrangement of the cubes?

This activity is based on an important task developed by Battista (1999) to engage students in grades 4 and 5 actively in developing a sense of the meaning of volume. Students who are given this task are also given physical models of the pattern pictures that they can cut out, use to make the 3-D box in the box picture, and fill with cubes. Successfully determining the number of cubes needed to fill each box requires students to engage in a process of spatial structuring and coordinated counting strategies.

Notice the careful design of the task. For the first three boxes, students are given two different views of the box that they will build and fill with cubes. Later in the task, for boxes D and F, students are given only one view (and finally, for box F, just a description of the box). Moreover, the students are encouraged to initiate their own strategies for determining the number of cubes that can fit in a particular box. The students can then build each box and test to see whether their strategy allows them to determine the number of cubes correctly for a particular box. As noted by Battista (1999, p. 442),

> Because students' predictions were based on their mental models, making predictions encouraged them to reflect on and refine those mental models. Strategies were refined as students reflectively reorganized their models and schemes to better fit their experiences.

This process aligns with NCTM's (2000) Learning Principle: "Students must learn mathematics with understanding, actively building new knowledge from experience and prior knowledge" (p. 20). Offering carefully structured mathematical tasks to build on students' prior knowledge and help them refine, extend, and challenge their current reasoning is essential. Before undertaking the task shown in figure 5.3, students do not need to know the term *volume*. However, teachers can introduce them to the term and help them connect it with the process of determining the number of cubes inside a 3-D space during or following such an activity.

As observed in Chapter 4 regarding the structures of arrays for area, students may or may not have a proper visual image of the structure of the cubes in a box. They are likely to know that some cubes will be needed to fill a box but remain unsure how to organize this unknown quantity into a useful view of the arrangements of cubes.

Battista (1999) discusses the thinking demonstrated by two fifth-grade students, whom he refers to as N and P, as they made their initial determinations of the number of cubes in box A. He notes that N initially calculated the number of cubes in box A by counting the squares that figure 5.4 shows as shaded on the four side flaps of the pattern picture for box A. N then doubled this number to calculate the total number of cubes, stating "there's 2 little squares going up on each side, so you times them," and thus N obtained 24 cubes as the number needed to fill the box.

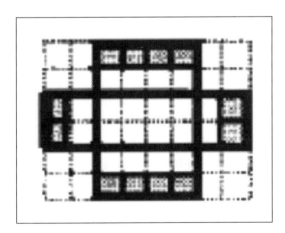

Fig. 5.4. The shaded squares represent N's initial count of squares on the side flaps. From Battista (1999, p. 421).

Battista (1999) observes that P, by comparison, counted the twelve visible faces on the box picture for A and then doubled that number to account for the hidden faces on the invisible sides of the box. Both students agreed that 24 was the correct number of cubes needed to fill box A. They then constructed box A and began to fill the box with cubes. Figure 5.5 shows an excerpt from the conversation, reported by Battista (1999), that developed between N and P after they attempted to fill box A with 24 cubes. Read through the excerpt, and pause to think about N's and P's reasoning as Reflect 5.2 suggests.

P: [*After putting 4 rows of 4 cubes into the box*] We're wrong. It's 4 sets of 4 equals 16.

N: What are we doing wrong? [*Neither student has an answer, so they move on to Box B.*]

P: What do you think we should do? [*For Box Picture B*] This is 1 box [*cube*], those 2 [*pointing at 2 visible faces of the cube at the bottom right front corner of Box Picture B*].

N: Oh, I know what we did wrong!

P: Is that what we did, at the corners?

N: Yeah, we counted this [*pointing to the front face of the bottom right front cube*] and then the side over there [*pointing to the right face of that cube*].

P: So we'll have to take away 4 [*pointing to the 4 vertical edges of Box Picture A*]; no, wait, we have to take away 8. [*P then subtracts 8 from their prediction of 24 and tells N that this subtraction would have made their prediction correct.*]

Fig. 5.5. N and P's conversation while working to fill boxes A and B.
From Battista (1999, p. 420).

Reflect 5.2

How would you characterize the understandings and misunderstandings that students N and P demonstrated as they attempted to determine the number of cubes that would fill box A?

Both N and P made incorrect calculations as they attempted to predict the number of cubes needed for box A. They did not have a way of visualizing the cubes in the box that allowed them to determine the volume correctly. They focused primarily on the faces of the cubes without considering the arrangement of the cubes.

When they realized that they had arrived at the incorrect number of cubes, P suggested that double-counting the corners was the reason for their erroneous result.

Noting that the corners of the box have eight cubes (that is, a cube on each of the box's eight vertices), he suggested subtracting 8 to address the double-counting and arrive at the correct result of 16 cubes. The students attempted to coordinate their views of the arrangement of the cubes and their calculations with their experiences of trying to fill the box.

However, their current structuring of the cube arrangement proved insufficient for boxes B and C. As N and P worked on these boxes, they continued to consider how to address the challenge of coordinating their structuring, their calculations, and their experiences of the number of cubes. N and P persisted in their strategy of using the exposed faces on the box picture and trying to compensate for double-counting the cubes. However, they recognized the difficulties they had in determining the number of cubes "in the middle" of the box.

Note that the design of this task promotes making a conjecture about the number of cubes and then building the box and filling it with cubes, thus allowing students to recognize faulty strategies. When N and P moved to box D, N arrived at a new strategy for counting the number of cubes, as detailed in the excerpt of dialogue between N and P (Battista 1999) in figure 5.6 (speaker R in the excerpt is the researcher). Respond to the questions in Reflect 5.3 after reading the dialogue.

N: I think I know Box D; I think it's going to be 30. Here, it goes 2 up [*pointing to a column in the upper flap of Pattern Picture D*]. So 5 plus 5 plus 5 [*pointing to the columns in the pattern's middle*], 15. And it's 2 high. Then you need to do 3 more rows of that because you need to do the top; 20, 25, 30 [*pointing to middle columns again*].

P: I don't know—that'd probably work, I guess.

R: How did you think of this new idea?

N: I just saw it on Box D, and then I tried it on Box C, and it worked.

[*P counts cube rows as he removes them from the box—5, 10, . . . , 30. Both boys smile.*]

P: Explain that to me again.

N: There's 2 rows here, going up [*motioning along the left column of the upper flap*]. There's 2 rows going up [*pointing to a 2-by-1 column in one of the 2-by-3 sides of Box D*], and there's 3 rows here of 5 [*pointing along a row of 3 in the box's bottom*]; 5, 10, 15; there's 15 down there [*pointing to the bottom of the box*]. Then there's another 15 there [*pointing to the top row of the 2-by-3 side*], and that's 30.

Fig. 5.6. N and P's conversation (with an interjection from the researcher as speaker R) about box pattern D. From Battista (1999, p. 425).

P: So there's 15 right here [*pointing to the bottom of the box*].

N: Yeah, on the bottom. And in the top part here [*motioning*] there'd be another 15.

P: All this top here [*motioning along the top rows of the sides of the box*]?

N: Yeah. See, you go 1, 2, . . . , 15 [*counting the squares on the bottom of the box*].

P: And then you add another 15.

Fig. 5.6. *Continued*

Reflect 5.3

How many cubes fit in box D? How would you characterize the understandings and misunderstandings of N and P as they attempt to determine the number of cubes in box D? How has their thinking changed from their thinking while working on boxes A–C?

With box D, N changed his view of the spatial structuring and began to visualize the cubes in the box in layers. He recognized that the box has two layers, since each of the flaps in the pattern has two rows of cubes for a box that is two cubes high. He then determined the number of cubes on the bottom layer, referring to the 3 rows of 5 cubes and counting them one at a time to confirm that the bottom layer has 15 cubes. P was initially uncertain, though willing to go along, but he became much more interested in N's strategy when he recognized that it was generating correct results. Note that N was developing the type of spatial structuring needed for a deep understanding of volume. N began by viewing the arrangement of cubes in layers, with a 3-by-5 arrangement of cubes on the bottom layer. He recognized that this layer was repeated again in the second layer of cubes, causing him to double the number of cubes that he determined in the first layer (resulting in a total of 30 cubes).

Figure 5.7 shows a box picture for a different box, which Reflect 5.4 asks you to refer to as you think further about the layering strategy for determining the number of cubes in figure 5.7.

Reflect 5.4

Examine the box picture in figure 5.7, and find all the possible ways that a student could view the cubes as layers to correctly determine the number of cubes that would fill the box.

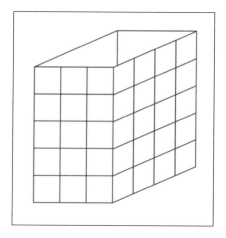

Fig. 5.7. A picture for a box to be filled with layers of cubes (see Reflect 5.4)

Students can view the layers of cubes in different ways as they coordinate the two-dimensional diagram with the three-dimensional unit for volume. For example, a student could view the bottom layer as 3 cubes by 4 cubes (that is, 12 total cubes) and consider that the box has 5 layers like this, prompting her to multiply 12 by 5, or $(3 \times 4) \times 5 = 12 \times 5 = 60$ total cubes. Or the student could view the 4-by-5 side of the box as a layer and recognize that the box has 3 such layers, motivating him to multiply $3 \times (4 \times 5) = 3 \times 20 = 60$ total cubes. Or the student could view the 3-by-5 side as a layer and note that the box has 4 such layers, supporting the calculation $(3 \times 5) \times 4 = 15 \times 4 = 60$ total cubes. Any of these views and strategies is viable. Each strategy involves coordinating a view of volume as layers and connects with the meaning of multiplication. Such models are often used to demonstrate the associative property of multiplication (e.g., $(3 \times 4) \times 5 = 3 \times (4 \times 5)$) since such a model could be constructed for any multiplicative situation with three positive values.

A deep understanding of volume involves coordinating the meaning of volume, the spatial structuring of the 3-D object, and the calculations performed to measure the object's volume (Battista 2007). Students who lack any of these elements are missing important components of their understanding of volume. You must assess your students' understanding of each of these components and provide instructional tasks that help students build understanding or strengthen any component that is weak. To assess students' grasp of the meaning of volume, you can ask them to consider various contexts that may or may not require them to focus on volume. For example, you might have them consider whether they would need to know the volume when asked to put a border around the room or to cover the floor of a room with tiles. To assess whether your students' spatial structuring is coordinated with their volume calculations, you might ask them to determine the numbers of cubes needed to fill 3-D rectangular prisms when given nets and 2-D drawings, similar to the pattern pictures and box pictures in figure 5.3.

Many mathematics textbooks that we examined while writing this book included a one-day lesson on the volume of rectangular prisms, moving very quickly from having students think about layers to performing calculations. Whether such lessons support the deep understanding that students need to develop is doubtful. By contrast, the tasks such as those designed by Battista (1999), shown in figure 5.3, are intended to motivate students to make a conjecture and verify the number of cubes that fit in a box. Such tasks are much more likely to help students toward the goal.

Students can also be asked to determine the number of cubes in nonstandard objects such as those shown in figure 5.2. Such tasks can give students insight that helps them coordinate spatial structuring and the calculations that they make to determine volume. It is important to continue to emphasize the meaning of volume (the amount of 3-D space that a shape occupies or holds, measured in cubic units) throughout such activities. To extend this idea further, you might encourage students to find all the rectangular prisms (with integer side lengths) that have a particular volume—for example, 24 cubic centimeters. For this activity, you could give students 24 cubes apiece and ask them to create different rectangular prisms.

Summarizing Pedagogical Content Knowledge to Support Big Idea 2 and Essential Understanding 2*a*

Teaching the mathematical ideas in this chapter requires specialized knowledge related to the four components presented in the Introduction: learners, curriculum, instructional strategies, and assessment. The four sections that follow summarize some examples of these specialized knowledge bases in relation to Big Idea 2 and Essential Understanding 2*a* in the case of volume. Although we separate them to highlight their importance, we also recognize that they are connected and support one another.

Knowledge of learners

A variety of issues are important to anticipate, address, and assess. Students need to have sufficient time to develop an understanding of the meaning of volume and processes for measuring volume. Students often struggle in the development of essential understandings related to volume of rectangular prisms. As illustrated by N and P's discussion shown in figure 5.5, students may determine volume by counting the visible faces on a 2-D diagram of a rectangular prism. Moreover, students may be able to calculate the volume of a rectangular prism when given a "box picture" but not when given a "box pattern" for the same box, or vice versa. Students may also attempt to apply the formula for calculating the volume of a rectangular prism to 3-D objects such as those shown in figure 5.2.

Knowledge of curriculum

Textbooks often fail to provide sufficient time for students to develop an understanding of volume. Furthermore, as Battista (2007) writes, "Many traditional curricula prematurely teach numerical procedures for geometric measurement" (pp. 892–93). Do your materials have a curricular sequence that makes sense and provides sufficient time for students to grasp these ideas? What models and representations do your materials use to help students build their understanding of the meaning of the volume of rectangular prisms and non-standard 3-D shapes (such as those shown in figure 5.2)? Do students have opportunities to make conjectures and work with physical models to compare results with their conjectures? Do they have opportunities to rearrange cubes to create other solids with the same volume (Hiebert 1981)?

Knowledge of instructional strategies

Teachers can draw on many and varied instructional strategies in helping their students develop understanding of volume. A few examples are highlighted here.

Throughout their work with volume, students should connect 2-D diagrams of 3-D objects, 3-D representations of the objects' volume, and symbolic representations of their volume calculations. As your students create 3-D representations from 2-D drawings, you should ask questions such as the following:

- "How did you figure out where to put each cube?"

- [*Pointing to a particular cube in a 2-D drawing*] "Where is this cube in your 3-D model?"

- "How many cubes are there in the bottom layer? How can you figure out how many cubes are in the bottom layer when you look at the picture of that rectangular prism?"

Students can build different rectangular prisms with cubes and compare their volumes, responding to questions such as, "Which prism has the largest volume? The smallest volume? How do you know?"

Knowledge of assessment

Giving students tasks that provide you with opportunities to assess whether they are developing essential understandings related to volume is important. In grades 3–5, this means providing students with tasks such as the activity in figure 5.3, which has the potential to reveal students' understanding of volume in relation to rectangular prisms. As Battista (2007, p. 897) explains,

> Genuine understanding of volume measurement requires comprehending (a) what the attribute of volume is and how it behaves (i.e., conserving it as it is moved about and decomposed/recomposed), (b) how volume is measured by iterating units of volume, (c) how numerical processes can be used to determine volume measures for special classes of shapes, and (d) how these numerical processes are represented with words and algebra.

The transcript of N and P's conversation in figure 5.6 shows how these students developed an understanding of iterating (or making a second copy) of the bottom layer of cubes for box D. The task in figure 5.3 provides an opportunity for the teacher to assess whether the students have developed an understanding of iterating units of volume and relating volume to multiplication as outlined by CCSSM: "Relate volume to the operations of multiplication and addition and solve real world and mathematical problems involving volume" (NGA Center and CCSSO, 5.MD.5; also shown in fig. 5.1). In addition, this task provides an opportunity to observe which attributes of the box pictures and box patterns the students used in developing their strategies. For example, when students such as N count the 12 visible squares on the two faces of box A to determine the volume, teachers can see whether students have developed an understanding of the meaning of volume measure.

Conclusion

The recommendations from Battista (1999, 2007) and others demonstrate the value of introducing students to the big ideas and essential understandings related to volume. Developing these understandings requires giving students worthwhile tasks, opportunities to use physical models, and sufficient instructional time.

The next chapter—the last in this book—highlights the alignment of the essential understandings discussed in the preceding chapters with mathematical concepts and topics that students encounter at lower and higher levels of learning.

Chapter 6
Looking Back and Looking Ahead with Geometry and Measurement

This chapter highlights how the essential understandings for geometry and measurement in Chapters 1–5 align with ideas that students develop before and after grades 3–5. The chapter begins with a discussion of foundational understandings that students are expected to build in kindergarten through grade 2. When you encounter students in grades 3–5 who have gaps in their knowledge, you may need to assess their understanding of the ideas that this first section highlights. The second section discusses how the essential understandings discussed in Chapters 1–5 connect with mathematics that students learn beyond fifth grade. This discussion demonstrates how important it is for students in grades 3–5 to develop a deep understanding of the essential concepts that serve as a foundation for subsequent learning in geometry and measurement.

Supporting Knowledge in K–Grade 2 for Geometry and Measurement in Grades 3–5

Teachers in kindergarten through grade 2 can support the development of students' essential understandings of geometry and measurement in grades 3–5. According to the National Research Council Committee on Early Childhood Mathematics (2009), "Mathematics experiences in early childhood settings should concentrate on (1) number (which includes whole number, operations, and relations) and (2) geometry, spatial relations, and measurement" (p. 3). In the early grades, helping students establish a foundational understanding of geometric shapes, visualization and spatial reasoning, and attributes is important (Clements and Sarama 2004) so that they can build on it in grades 3–5. In the following sections, we discuss these aspects of foundational understanding in greater detail.

Focusing on shape

The Common Core State Standards (CCSSM; National Governors Association Center for Best Practices and Council of Chief State School Officers [NGA Center and CC-SSO] 2010) expect students in K–grade 2 to (1) identify and describe shapes (kindergarten); (2) analyze, compare, create, and compose shapes (kindergarten); and (3) reason with shapes and their attributes (grades 1 and 2); figure 6.1 shows the full statements of these standards. As discussed in Chapter 1, size and orientation are important considerations as young children identify and describe shapes. CCSSM's expectation for kindergartners is that they will "correctly name shapes regardless of their orientations or overall size" (NGA Center and CCSSO 2010, K.G.2, p. 12). Indeed, Clements and Sarama (2004) suggest that children as young as two or three years old should match shapes, first with the same size and orientation and then with different sizes and orientations. They also suggest that in K–grade 2, students should be able to "name circle, square, triangle, and rectangle in any *size* or *orientation* (varying shapes for triangles and rectangles)" (p. 44). If students have not had sufficient experience in K–2 to consider size and orientation of shapes, it is not surprising that they will come to grades 3–5 with the misconceptions demonstrated in Chapter 1.

Common Core State Standards for Mathematics, K–2

Kindergarten, Geometry (K.G)

Identify and describe shapes (squares, circles, triangles, rectangles, hexagons, cubes, cones, cylinders, and spheres).

1. Describe objects in the environment using names of shapes, and describe the relative positions of these objects using terms such as *above, below, beside, in front of, behind,* and *next to.*

2. Correctly name shapes regardless of their orientations or overall size.

3. Identify shapes as two-dimensional (lying in a plane, "flat") or three-dimensional ("solid").

Analyze, compare, create, and compose shapes.

4. Analyze and compare two- and three-dimensional shapes, in different sizes and orientations, using informal language to describe their similarities, differences, parts (e.g., number of sides and vertices/"corners") and other attributes (e.g., having sides of equal length).

Fig. 6.1. Geometry in grades K–2. CCSSM K.G.1–3, 4–6, 1.G.1, 2, 2.G.1
(NGA Center and CCSSO 2010, pp. 12, 16, and 20).

Common Core State Standards for Mathematics, K–2

Analyze, compare, create, and compose shapes, *continued*

5. Model shapes in the world by building shapes from components (e.g., sticks and clay balls) and drawing shapes.

6. Compose simple shapes to form larger shapes. *For example, "Can you join these two triangles with full sides touching to make a rectangle?"*

Grade 1, Geometry (1.G)

Reason with shapes and their attributes.

1. Distinguish between defining attributes (e.g., triangles are closed and three-sided) versus non-defining attributes (e.g., color, orientation, overall size); build and draw shapes to possess defining attributes.

2. Compose two-dimensional shapes (rectangles, squares, trapezoids, triangles, half-circles, and quarter-circles) or three-dimensional shapes (cubes, right rectangular prisms, right circular cones, and right circular cylinders) to create a composite shape, and compose new shapes from the composite shape.

Grade 2, Geometry (2.G)

Reason with shapes and their attributes.

1. Recognize and draw shapes having specified attributes, such as a given number of angles or a given number of equal faces. Identify triangles, quadrilaterals, pentagons, hexagons, and cubes.

Fig. 6.1. *Continued*

Children in K–grade 2 should also have opportunities to identify shapes in their environments as well as build, draw, manipulate, and describe shapes. These types of opportunities provide a foundation for them to sort, analyze, compare, and classify shapes as well as examine properties of shapes as discussed in Chapter 3. Students should also work to compose and decompose shapes. Clements and Sarama (2004) provide developmental guidelines for children aged 2–7 years. They suggest that children begin with using shapes to make a picture. As discussed earlier, students in K–grade 2 need opportunities to see, name, and create shapes in a variety of positions and orientations. Teachers must model the use of appropriate descriptions of these shapes. For example, a student may comment that rectangles have "two long sides and two short sides." The teacher must *not* support (or introduce) this misconception but instead could respond, "This is true for many rectangles, but here [drawing a square] is another rectangle where all sides are the same length."

In addition to describing shapes that they see in their environments, students can also be encouraged to describe shapes that are hidden from sight. For example, a teacher might place a "mystery" block in a sock or paper bag and ask a student to put a hand in the bag, feel the shape's features, and describe the shape. Clements and Sarama (2004) also suggest that students in K–grade 2 match 2-D shapes to identify congruent and noncongruent shapes. These types of activities support the development of students' understanding of geometric shapes and properties in grades 3–5.

Focusing on attributes

A fundamental idea that is introduced in K–grade 2 is that identifying the attribute that is being measured is important. For example, students in these early grades can consider their height, weight, and temperature, recognizing that height, weight, and temperature are different attributes that they can identify. This work lays the foundation for considering new attributes in grades 3–5, such as area and volume. Similarly, the process of measuring length provides a backdrop for the measurement processes for area and volume. Students identify a unit and iterate (make repeated copies) of the unit without overlaps or gaps. They use various units to estimate the length of a given object and consider what unit makes sense for a particular measurement task. They use informal measurement techniques and approximations of particular units that provide reasonable values, depending on the precision required for a given situation.

Students in K–grade 2 also begin to develop reasonable estimates for measures and for units, recognizing, for example, that 8 feet is a reasonable height for their classroom but 8 inches is not. They apply numbers to quantify the attributes of length (for instance, 4 feet), capacity (2 liters or 12 gallons, for example), and weight (for instance, 3 ounces or 30 pounds). The accuracy of their estimations increases as they gain a better sense of how great particular units are by using these units in various situations.

As students move into grades 3–5, recognizing that the attributes of area and volume are related to, but not the same as, the attribute of length becomes important. The crucial work in grades 3–5 involves contrasting prior knowledge of length with emerging understanding of these new attributes. As Chapter 4 makes plain, considerable confusion occurs when students lack a deep understanding of the difference between area and perimeter.

Extending Knowledge of Geometry in Grades 6–8

The geometric understanding that is developed in grades 3–5 lays the foundation for the geometric ideas that students will develop in grades 6–8. Two primary aspects of geometry and measurement provide this foundation: (a) properties of 2-D and 3-D shapes, and (b) measurement ideas and spatial structuring. The sections that follow offer further connection with the essential understandings and the Common Core State Standards for Mathematics (NGA Center and CCSSO 2010).

Building on understanding of properties of 2–D and 3–D shapes

When students progress from grades 3–5 to grades 6–8, they begin to examine objects in a class of shapes and to conjecture about what must stay the same (the invariant conditions) and what can change (the variant conditions) for an object to remain in the same class. Students in the middle grades examine additional properties of shapes, including reflectional and rotational symmetry. Students in grades 3–5 develop a foundational understanding of properties of figures and classes of shapes (recognizing, for example, all rectangles or all rectangular prisms), whereas students in grades 6–8 focus on conditions that may result in the construction of a unique shape, a class of shapes, or no shape that meets particular conditions. They explore these conditions experimentally with physical or virtual tools, as CCSSM expects (see fig. 6.2).

Common Core State Standards for Mathematics, Grade 7

Draw, construct, and describe geometrical figures and describe the relationships between them.

2. Draw (freehand, with ruler and protractor, and with technology) geometric shapes with given conditions. Focus on constructing triangles from three measures of angles or sides, noticing when the conditions determine a unique triangle, more than one triangle, or no triangle.

Fig. 6.2. Drawing geometric shapes under given conditions.
CCSSM 7.G.2 (NGA Center and CCSSO 2010, p. 50).

For example, middle-grades students might consider triangles that have an angle that measures 40 degrees and an angle that measures 50 degrees. In response to the question, "What is true of all these triangles?" they might observe that these triangles are all right triangles that are similar, perhaps going on to say that a scale factor could be used to describe the relationship between the corresponding sides for any two of these triangles. Or they might be asked, "What triangles could be constructed that have at least two right angles?" (In Chapter 2 we discussed posing similar questions to students in grades 3–5.) In this case, teachers would want students to recognize that no triangle can have two or more right angles—at least not in the world of Euclidean geometry in which mathematicians typically work.

Students in grades 6–8 examine the impact of decomposing and rearranging as described in *Developing Essential Understanding of Geometry for Teaching Mathematics in Grades 6-8* (Sinclair, Pimm, and Skelin 2012) as well as the areas and volumes of various figures in relation to their dimensions. For example, they might explore the area of triangles that have the same base and height, such as triangles *DCB*, *ACB*, *ECB*, and *FCB* in figure 6.3. Through these explorations, they will discover that such triangles have the same area.

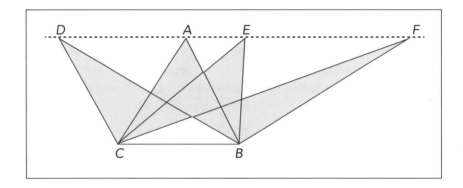

Fig. 6.3. Triangles with the same area. From Sinclair, Pimm, and Skelin (2012, p. 19).

Building an understanding of what is meant by *triangle* and *area* is fundamental and essential to the mathematical growth of all students. Work in grades 3–5 focuses on developing students' understanding of the meaning of *triangle* so that they move beyond the all-too-typical view of a triangle as equilateral with a base that is parallel to the foot of the page on which it is represented. Furthermore, students in grades 3–5 must develop a robust understanding of *area* as described in Chapter 4 and recognize that when they compare the areas of two shapes, they are comparing the sizes of the interior regions of the shapes and typically will measure them in square units. In grades 6–8, students extend their understanding to describe relationships among shapes to compare their areas. For example, students can recognize the relationship between the areas of a parallelogram and a triangle that have equal heights and bases with the same length.

Visualizing geometric relationships is another part of the work that students do in grades 3–5 that allows them to move to more advanced work in grades 6–8. Students can visualize rectangles being stretched or rotated and recognize that such transformations may or may not result in shapes that are rectangles. In grades 6–8, students begin to visualize the relationship between 2-D nets and the 3-D shapes that could be composed from them. For example, students could examine the nets in figure 6.4 and determine which of these nets could be used to form a cube.

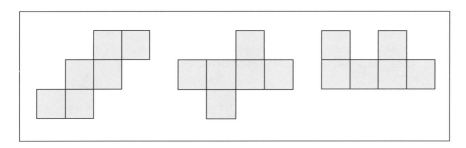

Fig. 6.4. Nets that students might examine to determine which they could use to form a cube

Students in grades 3–5 should have experiences that encourage them to visualize various shapes and other geometric relationships. Visualization is an essential part of geometric thinking at all levels and should be linked to all aspects of geometric reasoning in grades 3–5.

Another important aspect of geometry in grades 6–8 involves deepening students' understanding of transformations, including reflections, rotations, and dilations. This relates to the work done in grades 3–5, since students' conceptions of angles (see Chapter 2) directly affect their understanding of rotations. Students in grades 6–8 examine various transformations, consider how these transformations alter the properties of shapes, and connect the transformations to new ideas that they are learning about ratios and proportions. CCSSM expects students to recognize, for example, that some transformations result in an image that is *congruent* (same size and same shape) to the original shape; figure 6.5 shows the standard. Chapter 3 describes experiences in grades 3–5 (see fig. 3.20, for example) that help students recognize that rectangles are still rectangles when their orientation is changed. These ideas lay the foundation for formal recognition of the idea that particular transformations, such as reflections and rotations, result in congruent figures.

Common Core State Standards for Mathematics, Grade 8

Understand congruence and similarity using physical models, transparencies, or geometry software.

2.   Understand that a two-dimensional figure is congruent to another if the second can be obtained from the first by a sequence of rotations, reflections, and translations; given two congruent figures, describe a sequence that exhibits the congruence between them.

Fig. 6.5. Recognizing congruence through rotations, reflections, and translations. CCSSM 8.G.2 (NGA Center and CCSSO 2010, p. 55).

Building on measurement ideas involving iterating and spatial structuring

Students' work in grades 3–5 with measurement—primarily, perimeter, area, and volume—develops a foundation for further work with measurement in grades 6–8. Students must construct a sound understanding of these essential ideas in the elementary grades so that they can build on this understanding as they encounter more challenging concepts in the middle grades. In grades 6–8, students determine the area of shapes by applying the meaning of area and recognizing that area involves determining the number of square units that are needed to cover a surface, as CCSSM recommends, as shown in figure 6.6.

Common Core State Standards for Mathematics, Grade 6

Solve real-world and mathematical problems involving area, surface area, and volume.

1.   Find the area of right triangles, other triangles, special quadrilaterals, and polygons by composing into rectangles or decomposing into triangles and other shapes; apply these techniques in the context of solving real-world and mathematical problems.

Fig. 6.6. Solving problems involving area, CCSSM 6.G.1 (NGA Center and CCSSO 2010, p. 44).

As students grow in their understanding, they can compare areas of shapes to determine whether the area of a familiar figure is more or less than that of a given shape. For example, students might determine the area of a trapezoid by using what they know about rectangles and decomposing the trapezoid into a rectangle and two triangles, as illustrated in figure 6.7.

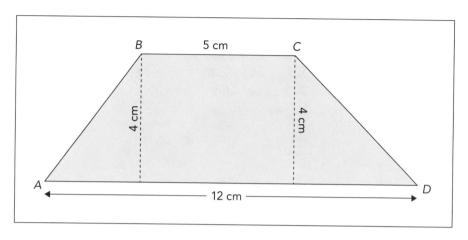

Fig. 6.7. Trapezoid decomposed into a rectangle and two triangles.
From Page, Wagreich, and Chval (1993b, p. 94).

Alternatively, they could encase the trapezoid in a rectangle and subtract the area of the two added triangles from the area of the encasing rectangle to find the area of the trapezoid, as illustrated in figure 6.8. Recognizing that they can decompose a figure and rearrange its area without changing the total area is a critical insight for students in grades 3–5. This idea can become concrete and explicit to students when they cut apart and compare the areas of various figures.

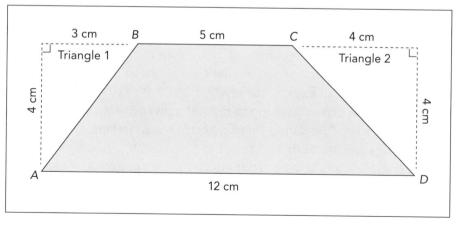

Fig. 6.8. Trapezoid encased in a rectangle.
From Page, Wagreich, and Chval (1993b, p. 95).

Likewise, students' experiences with volume in grades 3–5 support more complex work with volume in grades 6–8. As with area, students can draw on and extend the meaning that they began to ascribe to volume in grades 3–5, recognizing that volume involves determining the number of cubic units. Further, their spatial structuring of layers of cubes (see Chapter 5) lays the foundation for their consideration of the volume of any prism as they determine the number of cubes needed for the area of the base of the prism and the number of layers needed for its height. Figure 6.9 shows CCSSM's expectation for students in grade 6 with respect to volume.

Common Core State Standards for Mathematics, Grade 6

Solve real-world and mathematical problems involving area, surface area, and volume.

2. Find the volume of a right rectangular prism with fractional edge lengths by packing it with unit cubes of the appropriate unit fraction edge lengths, and show that the volume is the same as would be found by multiplying the edge lengths of the prism. Apply the formulas $V = l\,w\,h$ and $V = b\,h$ to find volumes of right rectangular prisms with fractional edge lengths in the context of solving real-world and mathematical problems.

Fig. 6.9. Exploring volume by layering with cubes and applying the formulas for volume. CCSSM 6.G.2 (NGA Center and CCSSO 2010, p. 45).

Furthermore, students build on the knowledge that they bring from grades 3–5 as they compare the volume of a rectangular prism with the volume of a pyramid with the same base and height and recognize that the volume of the pyramid is less than that of the prism. They can explore the relationship that exists between a pyramid and the corresponding prism. Note again that an understanding of the meaning of volume is the critical foundation that supports these relationships. Too many students lack this understanding and resort to memorizing rules, a step that is not only a chore but also leads to superficial understanding of area and volume with little long-term retention of information.

As students progress through grades 6–8, they develop generalized rules—formulas—for determining the area of various 2-D shapes. Such rules require students to recognize relationships among shapes and consider the effects that changes can have on their areas. They must draw on their knowledge of the meaning of area, their understanding of various types of figures, and the meaning of the operations. For instance, to understand the area of a trapezoid and generalize a formula, they need to draw on their understanding of all different types of trapezoids and the meaning of multiplication and addition in relation to area. Students might recognize, for example, that the trapezoids in figure 6.10 all have the same area and consider efficient ways to determine the area of any trapezoid, when given the height and lengths of both bases.

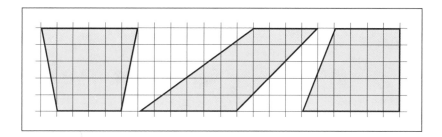

Fig. 6.10. Three trapezoids with heights and bases that are the same lengths

General formulas for volume also emerge from and build on students' prior work in grades 3–5 with rectangular prisms. Students use the formulas that they developed for the area of a rectangle to determine the formula for the volume of a square pyramid, and they build on their knowledge of areas of rectangles and triangles to find the surface areas of rectangular prisms, pyramids, and cylinders. Students can also consider the impact that increasing the volume of various 3-D figures has on their surface areas, recognizing from their previous work that a change in the area of a figure does not necessarily lead to an increase in its perimeter.

Conclusion

Just a few examples from the content in grades 6–8 show that the understanding of geometry and measurement that students develop in grades 3–5 is essential to the learning that follows. Students' work with shape and measurement in grades 3–5 provides a starting point in grades 6–8 for reasoning about various mathematical topics, such as congruence, similarity, transformations, measurement, and classification. Moreover, the work that students do in grades 3–5 influences their reasoning on tasks in a variety of mathematical strands, strengthening their work on contextualized problems in algebra and probability, and in justifying algorithms for multiplication and division of fractions (Lannin, Chval, and Jones 2013). Reasoning with shapes extends beyond the mathematical realm as well and has connections to diverse fields, such as art and design, architecture, engineering, chemistry, geography, and physics. Considerable time and effort are needed in grades 3–5 to develop an understanding that will be sufficiently robust to ensure that students will be successful in grades 6–8. As a teacher, you play a critical role in developing such understanding through your careful selection of instructional strategies and assessments, your use of your students' current and prior understanding, and your knowledge of curriculum.

Appendix 1
The Big Ideas and Essential Understandings for Geometry and Measurement

This book focuses on essential understandings that are identified and discussed in *Developing Essential Understanding of Geometry and Measurement for Teaching Mathematics in Grades 3–5* (Lehrer and Slovin 2014). For the reader's convenience, the full list of the big ideas and essential understandings in that book is reproduced below. The big ideas and essential understandings that are the special focus of this book are highlighted in orange.

Big Idea 1. Transforming objects and the space that they occupy in various ways while noting what does and does not change provides insight into and understanding of the objects and space.

> Essential Understanding 1*a*. Transformation supplies a dynamic basis for analyzing and describing a variety of situations and relationships.
>
> Essential Understanding 1*b*. Transformation offers a means by which to explain geometrical phenomena in ways that build on spatial intuitions.

Big Idea 2. One way to analyze and describe geometric objects, relationships among them, or the space that they occupy is to quantify—measure or count—one or more of their attributes.

> Essential Understanding 2*a*. Measurement can specify "how much" by assigning a number that corresponds to a chosen unit to such attributes as length, area, volume, and angle.
>
> Essential Understanding 2*b*. Geometry and measurement can precisely specify directions, routes, and locations in the world—for example, paths of navigation and coordinates describing spatial relationships.
>
> Essential Understanding 2*c*. Motion is useful in coordinating measurement and

generation of attributes of length, area, volume, and angle.

Essential Understanding 2*d*. Decomposing and composing objects facilitates their measurement, and using those decompositions and compositions to derive formulas clarifies relationships between quantified attributes and units of measure.

Big Idea 3. A classification scheme specifies the properties of objects that are relevant to particular goals and intentions.

Essential Understanding 3*a*. Classification schemes and associated defining properties depend on the purposes and contexts envisioned for mathematical investigation, and multiple classification schemes are often possible.

Essential Understanding 3*b*. Classification specifies relationships, such as equivalence and inclusion, within and between classes.

Essential Understanding 3*c*. Classification leads to investigation of criteria for particular classes of shapes, and such investigation can lead in turn to the identification of new properties and relationships among objects in the class.

Appendix 2
Resources for Teachers

The following list highlights a few of the many books, articles, and websites that are helpful resources for teaching geometry and measurement in grades 3–5. Abstracts from the publishers provide brief descriptions of the resources.

Books

Battista, Michael T. *Cognition-Based Assessment & Teaching of Geometric Measurement: Building on Students' Reasoning.* Portsmouth, N.H.: Heinemann, 2012.

———. *Cognition-Based Assessment & Teaching of Geometric Shapes: Building on Students' Reasoning.* Portsmouth, N.H.: Heinemann, 2012.

> Using a research-based framework that describes the development of students' thinking and learning in terms of levels of sophistication, a "cognitive terrain" that includes ascents and plateaus, Battista shows how teachers can build on their students' reasoning. His approach emphasizes three key components that support students' mathematical sense making and proficiency:
>
> - Determining students' levels of sophistication in reasoning
> - Assessing and monitoring the development of students' understanding of core ideas
> - Differentiating instruction to meet individual students' learning needs

Clements, Douglas H., and Julie Sarama. *Engaging Young Children in Mathematics: Standards for Early Childhood Mathematics.* Mahwah, N.J.: Lawrence Erlbaum, 2004.

> Two main parts and an online appendix (http://www.gse.buffalo.edu/org/conference/) compose this book. Part One, "Major Themes and Recommendations," offers a framework for thinking about pre-kindergarten–grade 2 mathematics education and specific recommendations. Part Two, "Elaboration of Major Themes and Recommendations," provides substantive detail regarding young students' understandings of mathematical ideas. The authors—
>
> - present comprehensive summaries of research that provide specific guidelines for standards, curriculum, and teaching;

- take recent reports and recommendations for early childhood mathematics education to the next level;

- integrate practical details and research;

- provide a succinct but thorough review of research on the topics, sequences, and learning trajectories that are appropriate for children at each year from age 2 to 7, with specific developmental guidelines that suggest suitable content for each topic for each year.

Driscoll, Mark. *Fostering Geometric Thinking: A Guide for Teachers, Grades 5–10.* Portsmouth, N.H.: Heinemann, 2007.

Anyone teaching geometry and measurement can discover essential, practical ideas in this book for helping students cultivate geometric habits of mind that lead to success in these fundamental mathematical topics. The author focuses on rigorous, problem-based teaching that encourages students to deepen their thinking in three key geometric strands:

- Geometric properties
- Geometric transformations
- Measurement of geometric objects

Discover how the interplay of these strands supports students in devising multiple solutions and developing a broader sense of geometric principles.

Lehrer, Richard, and Hannah Slovin. *Developing Essential Understanding of Geometry and Measurement for Teaching Mathematics in Grades 3–5.* Essential Understanding Series. Reston, Va.: National Council of Teachers of Mathematics, 2014.

This book focuses on essential knowledge for mathematics teachers about geometry and measurement. It is organized around three big ideas, supported by multiple smaller, interconnected ideas—*essential understandings*. Taking teachers beyond a simple introduction to geometry and measurement, the book aims to broaden and deepen their understanding of one of the most challenging topics for students— and teachers. Developing this understanding will help teachers engage students, anticipate their perplexities, avoid pitfalls, and dispel misconceptions. The book also suggests how to develop appropriate tasks, techniques, and tools for assessing students' understanding of the topics.

Usiskin, Zalman, and Jennifer Griffin. *The Classification of Quadrilaterals: A Study of Definition.* Charlotte, N.C.: Information Age, 2008.

This book reports on an analysis of a small part of the mathematics curriculum— the definitions given to quadrilaterals. Some disagreement exists about the definitions and, consequently, about the ways in which quadrilaterals are classified and relate to one another. The issues underlying these differences continually engage students, teachers, mathematics educators, and mathematicians. Numerous articles and essays address the definitions and classification of quadrilaterals, and curricular materials reflect the broad mathematical issues revolving around definitions.

The intended audience for this book includes curriculum developers, researchers, teachers, teacher trainers, and anyone interested in language and its use.

Van de Walle, John A., Karen S. Karp, and Jennifer M. Bay-Williams. *Elementary and Middle School Mathematics: Teaching Developmentally.* 7th ed. Needham Heights, Mass.: Allyn & Bacon, 2010.

The authors wrote this book to help teachers understand mathematics and become confident in their ability to teach the subject to children in kindergarten through eighth grade. The chapters related to the teaching and learning of geometric thinking, geometric concepts, and measurement concepts provide ideas and insights that can support teachers as they design and implement their lessons.

Articles

Battista, Michael T. "Understanding the Development of Students' Thinking about Length." *Teaching Children Mathematics* 13 (October 2006): 140–46.

Assessment tasks and a conceptual framework help teachers understand elementary students' thinking about the concept of length. The authors discuss common difficulties that students have with length and how to differentiate instruction to reach these learners.

Clements, Douglas, and Julie Sarama. "Young Children's Ideas about Geometric Shapes." *Teaching Children Mathematics* 6 (April 2000): 482–88.

Young children's thinking about geometric shapes is examined, as are implications for teaching and learning.

Jeon, Kyungsoon. "Mathematics Hiding in the Nets for a Cube." *Teaching Children Mathematics* 15 (March 2009): 394–99.

The author expands on a mathematical discussion among third graders in response to the question, "How many different nets can you draw that can fold into a cube?" The article also makes connections to other platonic solids and Euler's formula.

Keiser, Jane M., Amanda Klee, and Karen Fitch. "An Assessment of Students' Understanding of Angle." *Mathematics Teaching in the Middle School* 9 (October 2003): 116–19.

The authors discuss assessment tasks related to angles and classify students' definitions.

Mack, Nancy K. "Gaining Insights into Children's Geometric Knowledge." *Teaching Children Mathematics* 14 (November 2007): 238–45.

Research on children's geometric thinking was used in conjunction with the picture book *The Greedy Triangle* to gain valuable insights into children's early geometric understanding of polygons. The article includes a template for shape cards used in the activity discussed.

McCool, Jenni K., and Carol Holland. "Investigating Measurement Knowledge." *Teaching Children Mathematics* 18 (May 2012): 542–48.

Collaborating with a researcher, a teacher uses two fifth graders' assessment results to inform her whole-class instruction and gain insight into all her students' conceptual knowledge.

Munier, Valérie, Claude Devichi, and Hélène Merle. "A Physical Situation as a Way to Teach Angle." *Teaching Children Mathematics* 14 (March 2008): 402–7.

In a study of third- and fourth-grade students, a four-part lesson includes an experimental sequence that embeds the concept of angle. The students abstract this concept from the concrete, real-life situation and connect the physical experience with geometrical ideas.

Outhred, Lynne N., and Michael C. Mitchelmore. "Young Children's Intuitive Understanding of Rectangular Area Measurement." *Journal for Research in Mathematics Education* 31 (March 2000): 144–67.

The strategies that young children use to solve rectangular covering tasks before they have been taught area measurement are the focus of the authors' study. They observed 115 children from grades 1 to 4 as they solved various array-based tasks, and then they collected and analyzed their drawings and sorted their solution strategies into five developmental levels. They suggest that children sequentially learn four principles underlying rectangular covering. They emphasize the importance of understanding the relation between the size of the unit and the dimensions of the rectangle in learning about rectangular covering, clarify the role of multiplication, and identify the significance of a relational understanding of length measurement. Implications for the learning of area measurement are addressed.

Renne, Christine. "Is a Rectangle a Square? Developing Mathematical Vocabulary and Conceptual Understanding." *Teaching Children Mathematics* 10 (January 2004): 258–63.

Aiming to encourage students' thinking and conceptual development, a fourth-grade teacher examines classroom discourse and written work generated from her students' analysis and description of basic geometric shapes.

Sharp, Janet M., and Karen Bush Hoiberg. "And Then There Was Luke: The Geometric Thinking of a Young Mathematician." *Teaching Children Mathematics* 7 (March 2001): 432–39.

The authors use the van Hiele levels of geometric thinking to analyze the thinking of a student named Luke.

Tzur, Ron, and Matthew R. Clark. "Riding the Mathematical Merry-Go-Round to Foster Conceptual Understanding of Angle." *Teaching Children Mathematics* 12 (April 2006): 388–93.

> The authors provide activities to foster students' conceptual understanding of angle.

Whiten, David, and Phyllis Whiten. "Why Are Things Shaped the Way They Are?" *Teaching Children Mathematics* 15 (April 2009): 464–72.

> Important geometric concepts are embedded in the shape and design of natural and manufactured objects. After describing fourth graders' explorations of why manhole covers are circles, the authors then offer a range of activities to demonstrate how inquiring about shape in botany, geology, biology, and industry can effectively integrate science and mathematics and foster a lifelong spirit of inquiry.

Online Resources

NCTM Illuminations Lessons
http://illuminations.nctm.org/

> The NCTM Illuminations project originated as part of the Verizon Thinkfinity program and is designed, maintained, and continually expanded by NCTM. The website presents a variety of standards-based resources, including lessons, activities, and hundreds of Web links.

Illustrative Mathematics Project
http://www.illustrativemathematics.org

> Illustrative Mathematics provides guidance to states, assessment consortia, testing companies, and curriculum developers by illustrating the range and types of mathematical work that support implementation of the Common Core State Standards. One tool on this website is a growing collection of mathematical tasks that are organized by standard for each grade level and illustrate important features of the indicated standard or standards. The tasks on the website are not meant to be considered in isolation. Taken together in sets, these tasks are intended to illustrate a particular standard. Eventually, the site will showcase sets of tasks for each standard that—
>
> - illuminate the central meaning of the standard and also show connections with other standards;
> - clarify what is familiar about the standard and what is new with the advent of the Common Core State Standards;
> - include both teaching and assessment tasks; and
> - reflect the full range of difficulty that the standard expects students to master.

Appendix 3
Tasks

This book examines rich tasks that have been used in the classroom to bring to the surface students' understandings and misunderstandings about geometry and measurement. A sampling of these tasks is presented here, in the order in which they appear in the book:

Is It a Square?

Sizing Up the Angle

Characterizing Obtuse Angles

Draw It If You Can, Part 1

Draw It If You Can, Part 2

Drawing a Square, Given Two Points

Is This a Rectangle?

Using Clues to Classify Rectangles

Rectangle Drawings

Brian's Thinking about Perimeter and Area

Constructing with Cubes

At More4U, Appendix 3 includes all the tasks discussed in the book, formatted for classroom use and ready for printing.

Is It a Square?

Some students were talking about this shape:

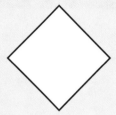

This is what they said:

Sarah: **The shape is a square because it has all sides the same length and 4 right angles.**

    Do you agree with Sarah?   Circle one: yes   no

    Explain your thinking.

Dudley: **The shape is NOT a square, but if you turn it, then it could be a square.**

    Do you agree with Dudley?   Circle one: yes   no

    Explain your thinking.

Marissa: **The shape is a diamond; it is not square.**

    Do you agree with Marissa?   Circle one: yes   no

    Explain your thinking.

Sizing Up the Angle

Look at angles *E* and *F*:

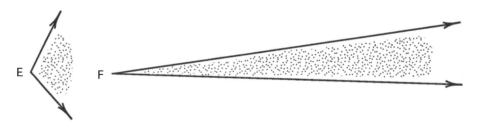

Which angle is larger?

Look at angles *Q, R, S, T, U,* and *V*:

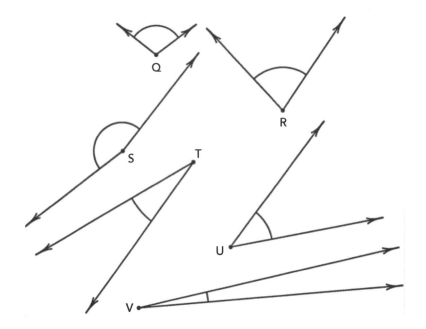

Which angle is smallest?

From *Maneuvers with Angles*, by David A. Page, Philip Wagreich, and Kathryn Chval (Parsippany, N.J.: Dale Seymour, 1993a, pp. 4, 18).

Characterizing Obtuse Angles

All the angles shown below are obtuse:

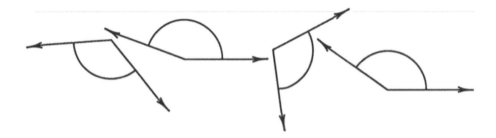

All the angles below are *not* obtuse:

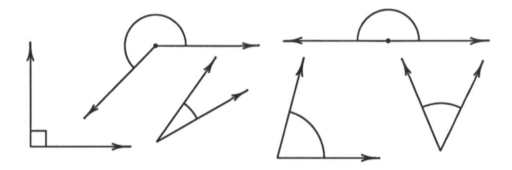

After looking at all these angles, write a description of an obtuse angle:

From *Maneuvers with Angles*, by David A. Page, Philip Wagreich, and Kathryn Chval (Parsippany, N.J.: Dale Seymour, 1993a, p. 12).

Draw It If You Can, Part 1

A. Draw a shape with 4 sides and no right angles.

B. Draw a triangle with 3 acute angles. If this is not possible, explain why.

C. Draw a triangle with 2 obtuse angles. If this is not possible, explain why.

Draw It If You Can, Part 2

A1. Draw a shape with 4 sides and only 1 right angle.

A2. Draw a shape with 4 sides and only 2 right angles.

A3. Draw a shape with 4 sides and only 3 right angles.

A4. Draw a shape with 4 sides and no obtuse angles.

A5. Draw a shape with 4 sides and no acute angles.

Drawing a Square, Given Two Points

Allie, Jack, and Emma explained their thinking about the following problem.

> Two points are shown.
> Draw a square that has these two points as two of its vertices.
>
> ●
>
>
> ●

a. *Allie said, "This is impossible. The two points are not in a straight line."*

Is Allie correct? Circle one: yes   no

Explain your thinking.

b. *Jack said, "Here is my square. It has 4 equal sides."*

Is Jack correct? Circle one: yes   no

Explain your thinking.

c. *Emma said, "My square has 4 right angles."*

Is Emma correct? Circle one: yes   no

Explain your thinking.

Adapted from Strutchens and Blume (1997, p. 169).

Is This a Rectangle?

Mary and Jeremiah were talking about this shape:

a. Mary says that the shape is a rectangle because the shape has 4 right angles and the opposite sides are the same length. Since this shape has these, it must be a rectangle.

Do you agree with Mary?   Circle one: yes   no

Explain your thinking.

b. Jeremiah says that it is not a rectangle because rectangles have two long sides and two short sides.

Do you agree with Jeremiah?   Circle one: yes   no

Explain your thinking.

Using Clues to Classify Rectangles

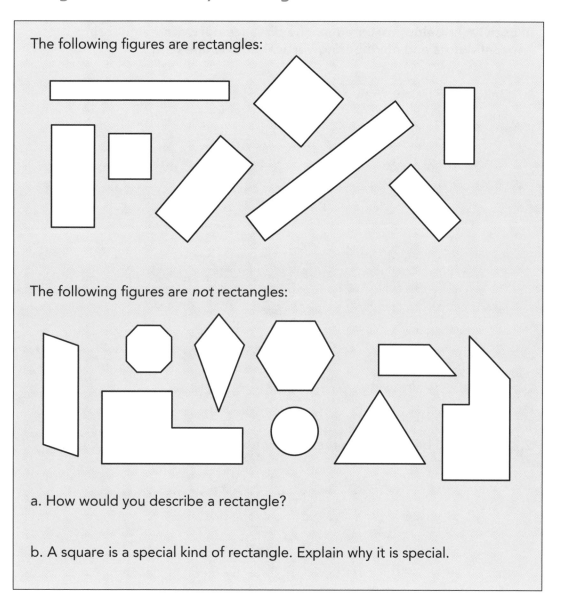

The following figures are rectangles:

The following figures are *not* rectangles:

a. How would you describe a rectangle?

b. A square is a special kind of rectangle. Explain why it is special.

From *Maneuvers with Rectangles*, by David A. Page, Philip Wagreich, and Kathryn Chval (Parsippany, N.J.: Dale Seymour, 1995, p. 13).

Rectangle Drawings

In both tasks below, assume that the distance between neighboring horizontal dots and neighboring vertical dots is one unit.

1. On the grid below, draw a rectangle with an area of 12 square units.

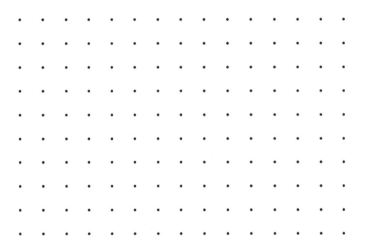

2. On the grid below, draw a rectangle with a perimeter of 14 units.

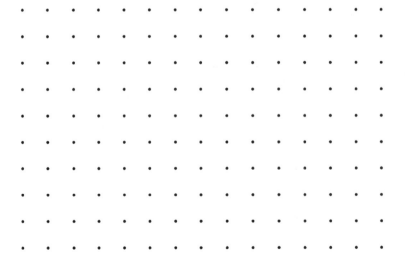

Brian's Thinking about Perimeter and Area

Brian looked at two rectangles, rectangle A and rectangle B. The perimeter of rectangle A was greater than the perimeter of rectangle B.

Brian said, "The area of rectangle A must be greater than the area of rectangle B."

Do you agree with Brian? Why or why not?

Constructing with Cubes

Look at the shapes in diagrams (a) and (b) below:

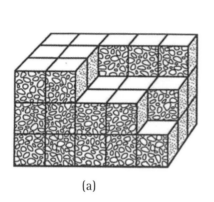 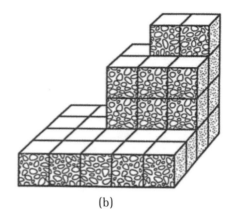

(a)   (b)

How many cubes would you need to build the shape in (a)?

How many cubes would you need to build the shape in (b)?

From *Maneuvers with Nickels and Numbers*, by David A. Page, Philip Wagreich, and Kathryn Chval (Parsippany, N.J.: Dale Seymour, 1993c, p. 54).

References

Ashlock, Robert B. *Error Patterns in Computation: Using Error Patterns to Improve Instruction.* 9th ed. Upper Saddle River, N.J.: Pearson, 2006.

Battista, Michael T. "Fifth Graders' Enumeration of Cubes in 3D Arrays: Conceptual Progress in an Inquiry-Based Classroom." *Journal for Research in Mathematics Education* 30 (July 1999): 417–48.

_____. "Understanding the Development of Students' Thinking about Length." *Teaching Children Mathematics* 13 (October 2006): 140–46.

_____. "The Development of Geometric and Spatial Thinking." In *Second Handbook of Research on Mathematics Teaching and Learning*, edited by Frank K. Lester, Jr., pp. 843–908. Charlotte, N.C.: Information Age, 2007.

_____. *Cognition-Based Assessment & Teaching of Geometric Shapes: Building on Students' Reasoning.* Portsmouth, N.H.: Heinemann, 2012a.

_____. *Cognition-Based Assessment & Teaching of Geometric Measurement: Building on Students' Reasoning.* Portsmouth, N.H.: Heinemann, 2012b.

Blume, Glendon W., Enrique Galindo, and Crystal Walcott. "Performance in Measurement and Geometry from the Viewpoint of *Principles and Standards for School Mathematics.*" In *Results and Interpretations of the 2003 Mathematics Assessment of the National Assessment of Educational Progress*, edited by Peter Kloosterman and Frank K. Lester, pp. 95–138. Reston, Va.: National Council of Teachers of Mathematics, 2007.

Burger, William F., and J. Michael Shaughnessy. "Characterizing the van Hiele Levels of Development in Geometry." *Journal for Research in Mathematics Education* 17 (January 1986): 31–48.

Carpenter, Thomas P. "Analysis and Synthesis of Existing Research on Measurement." In *Number and Measurement*, edited by Richard A. Lesh, pp. 47–83. Columbus, Ohio: ERIC Clearinghouse for Science, Mathematics, and Environmental Education, 1976.

Carpenter, Thomas P., Terrence G. Coburn, Robert E. Reys, and James W. Wilson. "Notes from National Assessment: Basic Concepts of Area and Volume." *Arithmetic Teacher* 22 (October 1975): 501–7.

Carpenter, Thomas P., Mary M. Lindquist, Catherine A. Brown, Vicky L. Kouba, Edward A. Silver, and Jane O. Swafford. "Results of the Fourth NAEP Assessment of Mathematics: Trends and Conclusions." *Arithmetic Teacher* 36 (December 1988): 38–41.

Clements, Douglas H., and Michael T. Battista. "Geometry and Spatial Reasoning." In *Handbook for Research on Mathematics Teaching*, edited by Douglas H. Grouws, pp. 420–64. New York: Macmillan, 1992.

Clements, Douglas H., and Barbara A. Burns. "Students' Development of Strategies for Turn and Angle Measure." *Educational Studies in Mathematics* 41, no. 1 (2000): 31–45.

Clements, Douglas H., and Julie Sarama, eds. *Engaging Young Children in Mathematics: Standards for Early Childhood Mathematics Education.* Mahwah, N.J.: Lawrence Erlbaum, 2004.

———. *Learning and Teaching Early Math: The Learning Trajectories Approach.* New York: Taylor & Francis, 2009.

Close, Gillian S. *Children's Understanding of Angle at the Primary/Secondary Transfer Stage.* London: Polytechnic of the South Bank, 1982.

Doig, Brian, Jill Cheeseman, and John Lindsay. "The Medium Is the Message: Measuring Area with Different Media." In *GALTHA: Proceedings of the 18th Annual Conference of the Mathematics Education Research Group of Australasia*, edited by Bill Atweh and Steve Flavel, vol. 1, pp. 229–40. Darwin, Australia: Mathematics Education Research Group of Australasia, 1995.

Dougherty, Barbara J. "Access to Algebra: A Process Approach." In *The Future of the Teaching and Learning of Algebra*, edited by Helen Chick, Kaye Stacey, Jill Vincent, and John Vincent, pp. 207–13. Melbourne, Victoria, Australia: University of Melbourne, 2001.

Driscoll, Mark. *Fostering Geometric Thinking: A Guide for Teachers, Grades 5–10.* Portsmouth, N.H.: Heinemann, 2007.

Edwards, Barbara S., and Michael B. Ward. "Surprises from Mathematics Education Research: Student (Mis)use of Mathematical Definitions." *American Mathematical Monthly* 111 (May 2004): 411–24.

Fosnot, Catherine Twomey, and Maarten Dolk. *Young Mathematicians at Work: Constructing Fractions, Decimals, and Percents.* Portsmouth, N.H.: Heinemann, 2002.

Foxman, Derek, and Graham Ruddock. "Assessing Mathematics: 3. Concepts and Skills: Line Symmetry and Angle." *Mathematics in Schools* 13 (March 1984): 9–13.

Fuys, David, Dorothy Geddes, and Rosamond Tischler. *The van Hiele Model of Thinking in Geometry among Adolescents. Journal for Research in Mathematics Education* Monograph Series, no. 3. Reston, Va.: National Council of Teachers of Mathematics, 1988.

Grossman, Pamela L. *The Making of a Teacher: Teacher Knowledge and Teacher Education.* Professional Development and Practice Series. New York: Teachers College Press, 1990.

Gutiérrez, Angel, and Adela Jaime. "On the Assessment of the van Hiele Levels of Reasoning." *Focus on Learning Problems in Mathematics* 20, nos. 2 and 3 (1998): 27–46.

Hart, Kathleen, and Lesley Booth. "Which Comes First—Length, Area, or Volume?" *Arithmetic Teacher* 31, no. 9 (1984): 16–18, 26–27.

Hiebert, James. "Units of Measure: Results and Implications from National Assessment." *Arithmetic Teacher* 28, no. 6 (February 1981): 38–43.

Hill, Heather C., Brian Rowan, and Deborah Loewenberg Ball. "Effects of Teachers' Mathematical Knowledge for Teaching on Student Achievement." *American Educational Research Journal* 42 (Summer 2005): 371–406.

Joram, Elana, Kaveri Subrahmanyam, and Rochel Gelman. "Measurement Estimation: Learning to Map the Route from Number to Quantity and Back." *Review of Educational Research* 68, no. 4 (1998): 413–49.

Keiser, Jane M. "Struggles with Developing the Concept of Angle: Comparing Sixth-Grade Students' Discourse to the History of the Angle Concept." *Mathematical Thinking and Learning* 6, no. 3 (2004): 285–306.

Keiser, Jane M., Amanda Klee, and Karen Fitch. "An Assessment of Students' Understanding of Angle." *Mathematics Teaching in the Middle School* 9 (October 2003): 116–19.

Lannin, John, Kathryn Chval, and Dusty Jones. *Putting Essential Understanding of Multiplication and Division into Practice in Grades 3–5*. Putting Essential Understanding into Practice Series. Reston, Va.: National Council of Teachers of Mathematics, 2013.

Lannin, John, Amy Ellis, and Rebekah Elliot. *Developing Essential Understanding of Mathematical Reasoning for Teaching Mathematics in Prekindergarten–Grade 8*. Essential Understanding Series. Reston, Va.: National Council of Teachers of Mathematics, 2011.

Lehrer, Richard, Michael Jenkins, and Helena Osana. "Longitudinal Study of Children's Reasoning about Space and Geometry." In *Designing Learning Environments for Developing Understanding of Geometry and Space*, edited by Richard Lehrer and Daniel Chazan, pp. 137–67. Mahwah, N.J: Lawrence Erlbaum, 1998.

Lehrer, Richard, and Hannah Slovin. *Developing Essential Understanding of Geometry and Measurement for Teaching Mathematics in Grades 3–5*. Essential Understanding Series. Reston, Va.: National Council of Teachers of Mathematics, 2014.

Ma, Liping. *Knowing and Teaching Elementary Mathematics: Teachers' Understanding of Fundamental Mathematics in China and the United States*. Mahwah, N.J.: Lawrence Erlbaum, 1999.

Mack, Nancy K. "Gaining Insights into Children's Geometric Knowledge." *Teaching Children Mathematics* 14 (November 2007): 238–45.

Magnusson, Shirley, Joseph Krajcik, and Hilda Borko. "Nature, Sources, and Development of Pedagogical Content Knowledge for Science Teaching." In *Examining Pedagogical Content Knowledge*, edited by Julie Gess-Newsome and Norman G. Lederman, pp. 95–132. Dordrecht, The Netherlands: Kluwer Academic, 1999.

Marks, Genée, and Judith Mousley. "Mathematics Education and Genre: Dare We Make the Process Writing Mistake Again?" *Language and Education* 4, no. 2 (1990): 117–35.

Martin, W. Gary, and Marilyn E. Strutchens. "Geometry and Measurement." In *Results from the Seventh Mathematics Assessment of the National Assessment of Educational Progress*, edited by Edward A. Silver and Patricia A. Kenney, pp. 193–234. Reston, Va.: National Council of Teachers of Mathematics, 2000.

Mayberry, Joanne. "The van Hiele Levels of Geometric Thought in Undergraduate Pre-service Teachers." *Journal for Research in Mathematics Education* 14, no. 1 (January 1983): 58–69.

McCool, Jenni K., and Carol Holland. "Investigating Measurement Knowledge." *Teaching Children Mathematics* 18 (May 2012): 542–48.

Mitchelmore, Michael C. "Young Students' Concepts of Turning and Angle." *Cognition and Instruction* 16, no. 3 (1998): 265–84.

Mitchelmore, Michael C., and Paul White. "Development of Angle Concepts by Progressive Abstraction and Generalisation." *Educational Studies in Mathematics* 41, no. 3 (2000): 209–38.

Munier, Valérie, Claude Devichi, and Hélène Merle. "A Physical Situation as a Way to Teach Angle." *Teaching Children Mathematics* 14 (March 2008): 402–7.

National Council of Teachers of Mathematics (NCTM). *Principles and Standards for School Mathematics.* Reston, Va.: NCTM, 2000.

National Governors Association Center for Best Practices and Council of Chief State School Officers (NGA Center and CCSSO). *Common Core State Standards for Mathematics. Common Core State Standards (College- and Career-Readiness Standards and K-12 Standards in English Language Arts and Math).* Washington, D.C.: NGA Center and CCSSO, 2010. http://www.corestandards.org.

National Research Council. *Mathematics Learning in Early Childhood: Paths toward Excellence and Equity.* Committee on Early Childhood Mathematics, edited by Christopher T. Cross, Taniesha A. Woods, and Heidi Schweingruber. Center for Education, Division of Behavioral and Social Sciences and Education. Washington, D.C.: National Academies Press, 2009.

Outhred, Lynne N., and Michael C. Mitchelmore. "Young Children's Intuitive Understanding of Rectangular Area Measurement." *Journal for Research in Mathematics Education* 31 (March 2000): 144–67.

_____. "Students' Structuring of Rectangular Arrays." In *Proceedings of the 28th Annual Conference of the International Group for the Psychology of Mathematics Education,* edited by Marit Johnsen Høines and Anne Berit Fuglestad, vol. 3, pp. 465–72. Bergen, Norway: Bergen University College, 2004.

Page, David A., Philip Wagreich, and Kathryn Chval. *Maneuvers with Angles.* Parsippany, N.J.: Dale Seymour, 1993a.

_____. *Maneuvers with Triangles.* Parsippany, N.J.: Dale Seymour, 1993b.

_____. *Maneuvers with Nickels and Numbers.* Parsippany, N.J.: Dale Seymour, 1993c.

_____. *Maneuvers with Rectangles.* Parsippany, N.J.: Dale Seymour, 1995.

Piaget, Jean. *The Child's Conception of Number.* New York: W. W. Norton, 1965.

Piaget, Jean, Barbel Inhelder, and Alina Szeminska. *The Child's Conception of Geometry.* New York: Basic Books, 1960.

Popham, W. James. "Defining and Enhancing Formative Assessment." Paper presented at the CCSSO State Collaborative on Assessment and Student Standards FAST meeting, Austin, Tex., October 10–13, 2006.

Pugalee, David K. "Connecting Writing to the Mathematics Curriculum." *Mathematics Teacher* 90 (April 1997): 308–10.

Renne, Christine. "Is a Rectangle a Square? Developing Mathematical Vocabulary and Conceptual Understanding." *Teaching Children Mathematics* 10 (January 2004): 258–63.

Schifter, Deborah. "Learning Geometry: Some Insights Drawn from Teacher Writing." *Teaching Children Mathematics* 5 (February 1999): 360–66.

Shepard, Richard G. "Writing for Conceptual Development in Mathematics." *Journal of Mathematical Behavior* 12, no. 3 (1993): 287–93.

Shulman, Lee S. "Those Who Understand: Knowledge Growth in Teaching." *Educational Researcher* 15 (1986): 4–14.

_____. "Knowledge and Teaching." *Harvard Educational Review* 57, no. 1 (1987): 1–22.

Silver, Edward A., Jeremy Kilpatrick, and Beth Schlesinger. *Thinking through Mathematics: Fostering Inquiry and Communication in Mathematics Classrooms.* New York: College Board, 1990.

Sinclair, Nathalie, David Pimm, and Melanie Skelin. *Developing Essential Understanding of Geometry for Teaching Mathematics in Grades 6–8.* Essential Understanding Series. Reston, Va.: National Council of Teachers of Mathematics, 2012.

Strutchens, Marilyn E., and Glendon W. Blume. "What Do Students Know about Geometry?" In *Results from the Sixth Mathematics Assessment of the National Assessment of Educational Progress,* edited by Patricia A. Kenney and Edward A. Silver, pp. 165–93. Reston, Va.: National Council of Teachers of Mathematics, 1997.

Suydam, Marilyn N. "The Shape of Instruction in Geometry: Some Highlights from Research." *Mathematics Teacher* 78 (September 1985): 481–86.

Tall, David, and Shlomo Vinner. "Concept Image and Concept Definition in Mathematics with Particular Reference to Limits and Continuity." *Educational Studies in Mathematics* 12, no. 2 (1981): 151–69.

Thompson, Tony D., and Ronald V. Preston. "Measurement in the Middle Grades: Insights from NAEP and TIMSS." *Mathematics Teaching in the Middle School* 9 (May 2004): 514–19.

Usiskin, Zalman. "Van Hiele Levels and Achievement in Secondary School Geometry." Final report of the Cognitive Development and Achievement in Secondary School Geometry Project. Chicago: University of Chicago, 1982. ERIC Document Reproduction Service ED 220 288.

Usiskin, Zalman, and Jennifer Griffin. *The Classification of Quadrilaterals: A Study of Definition.* Charlotte, N.C.: Information Age, 2008.

Van de Walle, John A., Karen S. Karp, and Jennifer M. Bay-Williams. *Elementary and Middle School Mathematics: Teaching Developmentally*. 7th ed. Needham Heights, Mass.: Allyn & Bacon, 2010.

van Hiele, Pierre M. "Development and the Learning Process." In *Acta Paedagogica Ultrajectina*, pp. 1–31. Groningen, The Netherlands: J. B. Wolters, 1959.

_____. *Structure and Insight.* New York: Academic Press, 1986.

van Hiele, Pierre M., and Dina van Hiele-Geldof. "A Method of Initiation into Geometry at Secondary Schools." In *Report on Methods of Initiation into Geometry*, edited by Hans Freudenthal, pp. 67–80. Groningen, The Netherlands: J. B. Wolters, 1958.

Vighi, Paola, and Carlo Marchini. "The Gap between Learning and Teaching Geometry." In *Proceedings of the Seventh Congress of the European Society for Research in Mathematics Education* (*CERME 7*), edited by Marta Pytlak, Tim Rowland, and Ewa Swoboda. Rzeszów, Poland: University of Rzeszów, 2011. http://www.cerme7.univ.rzeszow.pl/WG/4/WG4_Vighi.pdf.

Wiliam, Dylan. "Keeping Learning on Track: Classroom Assessment and the Regulation of Learning." In *Second Handbook of Research on Mathematics Teaching and Learning*, edited by Frank K. Lester, Jr., pp. 1053–98. Charlotte, N.C.: Information Age; Reston, Va.: National Council of Teachers of Mathematics, 2007.

Wilson, Patricia S., and Verna M. Adams. "A Dynamic Way to Teach Angle and Angle Measure." *Arithmetic Teacher* 39 (January 1992): 6–13.

Yinger, Robert J. "The Conversation of Teaching: Patterns of Explanation in Mathematics Lessons." Paper presented at the meeting of the International Study Association on Teacher Thinking, Nottingham, England, May 1988.

Titles in the Putting Essential Understanding into Practice Series

The Putting Essential Understanding into Practice Series takes NCTM's Essential Understanding Series to the next level through a focus on pedagogical content knowledge. Each volume builds on the companion volume in the earlier series to show teachers how to implement their understanding of mathematics in the classroom. The authors identify common misconceptions, along with strategies and activities to help students develop robust understanding through problem-based learning.

Putting Essential Understanding of—

Addition and Subtraction into Practice in Prekindergarten–Grade 2
ISBN 978-0-87353-730-8   Stock No. 14540

Fractions into Practice in Grades 3–5
ISBN 978-0-87353-732-2   Stock No. 14542

Multiplication and Division into Practice in Grades 3–5
ISBN 978-0-87353-715-8   Stock No. 14347

Ratios and Proportions into Practice in Grades 6–8
ISBN 978-0-87353-717-9   Stock No. 14349

Functions into Practice in Grades 9–12
ISBN 978-0-87353-714-8   Stock No. 14346

Statistics into Practice in Grades 9–12
ISBN 978-0-87353-737-7   Stock No. 14547

Geometry into Practice in Grades 9–12
ISBN 978-0-87353-736-0   Stock No. 14546

Geometry and Measurement into Practice in Grades 3–5
ISBN 978-0-87353-733-9   Stock No. 14543

Forthcoming:

Putting Essential Understanding of—

Number and Numeration into Practice in Prekindergarten–Grade 2

Geometry and Measurement into Practice in Prekindergarten–Grade 2

Expressions and Equations into Practice in Grades 6–8

Geometry into Practice in Grades 6–8

Visit www.nctm.org/catalog for details and ordering information.

Titles in the Essential Understanding Series

The Essential Understanding Series gives teachers the deep understanding that they need to teach challenging topics in mathematics. Students encounter such topics across the pre-K–grade 12 curriculum, and teachers who understand the big ideas related to each topic can give maximum support as students develop their own understanding and make vital connections.

Developing Essential Understanding of–

Visit www.nctm.org/catalog for details and ordering information.